WASTEWATER MICROBIOLOGY

Filamentous Bacteria Morphotype Indentification Techniques and Process Control Troubleshooting Strategies

Written by Ryan Hennessy

Edited by: Katharine Brien

Formatted by: Jordan Buchan
Rachel Mortimer

Table of Contents

About the Author

Hennessy has over 15 years of hands-on experience as a wastewater operator at various industrial and municipal treatment systems and more than 10 years conducting microscopy for thousands of wastewater treatment plants (mainly located within the United States and Canada). Hennessy was carefully trained by Dr. Richard to provide services for Dr. Richard's clients upon retirement. Additionally, Hennessy has conducted numerous on-site microscopy trainings for clients and educational presentations for various wastewater organizations since the early 2010s. Long term, Hennessy desires to be at the forefront of wastewater microscopy and troubleshooting for generations to come paying attention to new advances in technology and how and when they may be used to enhance wastewater treatment processes.

When not looking at "bugs" under the microscope Hennessy is a proud father and husband and enjoys watching his children's sports and other activities. Hennessy enjoys lifting weights, watching sports (in particular the Green Bay Packers and Milwaukee Bucks), and currently is developing his "old man" basketball game to continue playing in some bar 3 on 3 leagues into middle age (while hopefully avoiding injury!)

Dedications

This book is dedicated to Dr. Michael Richard for his help and mentorship over the years, as well as Hennessy's wife Brittany for her dedication and sacrifices to help Ryan focus on his career and still be blessed with a wonderful family, including Isaiah Hennessy, Noelle Hennessy, and dogs Tucker and Graycie.

Rest in Peace Dr. Michael Richard

Ryan Hennessy and Dr. Michael Richard circa 2014

On November 21st, 2021, the wastewater industry lost a legend, his family lost a great man, and I lost a mentor and close friend. I cannot thank Dr. Richard enough for his generosity in teaching me what he has learned in wastewater microbiology over the years and helping me navigate my career. While our relationship started off with me pestering him for wastewater knowledge, over the years our conversations became frequent, touching on all aspects of life. I couldn't even attempt to count the hours of time we have spent on the phone, in wastewater forums, exchanging email jokes, and him reviewing microbiology reports, always highly critical in a positive way, helping me learn.

I send my best wishes to his family and will always be thankful for the time and memories we shared together, as well as his generosity and tremendous impact on my career.

Introduction

The purpose of this textbook is to provide practical and straightforward knowledge for wastewater operators and professionals in the areas of wastewater microscopy and microbiology. It serves as a resource for wastewater process control and troubleshooting. This textbook includes training methods, filamentous bacteria morphotype identification strategies, and common problems encountered in wastewater treatment plants along with effective solutions.

Chapter 1:

Aerobic Biological Treatment Process Overview

Background

1.1 General Overview

1.2 Mixed Liquor

1.3 Critical Biomass

Background

This chapter will cover the basic principles of aerobic biological treatment processes. The chapter also serves as a brief introduction to this textbook. The objective of this textbook is to serve as a useful and practical reference for using wastewater microscopy as a tool to evaluate and troubleshoot wastewater treatment processes. The book concentrates on the biological secondary treatment process, as described below.

1.1 General Overview

Aerobic wastewater treatment processes act as an expedited way of replicating the treatment process that occurs naturally in bodies of water. There are many potential configurations of potential wastewater treatment process schematics, all of which contain a stage in which biological reactions occur and another stage in which final separations of liquid (i.e., treated water) and solids occur.

Raw or untreated wastewater generally undergoes some form of preliminary screening which may or may not be followed by a primary treatment process, such as primary clarifier(s) or DAF (dissolved air floatation) units. This text will not go into great detail about various configurations of wastewater treatment processes. However, the general concept in all processes is that organic material (or BOD) in the influent, when exposed to the necessary concentration of microorganisms and the proper conditions, is converted into new cellular mass, carbon dioxide, and water ("Respiration in bacteria: Microbiology," 2016). This is then followed by a step in which solids and/or microorganisms are separated from the now treated wastewater.

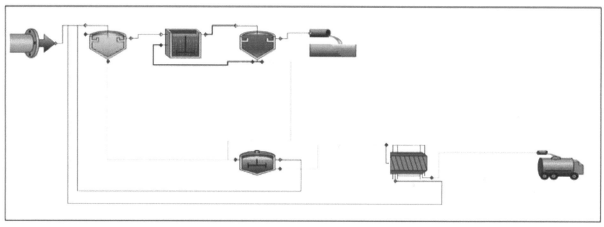

Diagram 1.0 The configuration above shows a basic and common configuration for many activated sludge processes. Image courtesy of Hydromantis: www.hydromantis.com

1.1A Primary Treatment

Most wastewater treatment processes are continual, where wastewater flows into a treatment plant based on flow from residential and/or industrial sources. For plants that have primary treatment (in diagram 1.1 a primary clarifier), the goal is initial separation of readily settleable solids and readily floatable material prior to entering the aeration basin. Floatable material is skimmed regularly and sludge that settles to the bottom of the tank is periodically pumped into an area for sludge treatment stabilization.

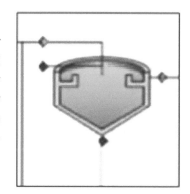

Diagram 1.1 Primary clarifier. Image courtesy of Hydromantis: www.hydromantis.com

1.1B Secondary Treatment

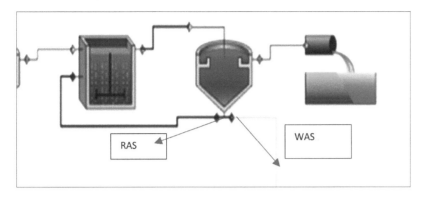

RAS

WAS

Diagram 1.2 Example Secondary Biological Treatment Process. Image courtesy of Hydromantis: www.hydromantis.com

The secondary treatment of wastewater is the focus of this textbook. Diagram 1.2 shows an aeration basin followed by a final clarifier. Influent wastewater enters the aeration basin, where it is exposed to microorganisms and the proper conditions in which the organic material in the influent is converted into new microorganism cell mass, water, and carbon dioxide, provided the proper conditions are present. As the amount of available food (i.e., organic material) in the influent decreases, the bacteria flocculate together so that they may settle by gravity in the downstream final clarifier. When the proper conditions (as described later within this chapter) occur, strong flocculation is expected (Nielsen et al., 2003).

The microorganisms (i.e. the mixed liquor) that become flocculated settle to the bottom of the clarifier and then are either returned (known as RAS: returned activated sludge) to the head of the aeration basin or wasted (known as WAS: wasted activated sludge) in order to obtain the proper concentration of desired bacteria within the aeration basin. Clear water, which is separated from the mixed liquor in the final clarifier, is then discharged to a receiving body, either a natural one or another wastewater treatment plant.

1.1C Sludge Treatment and Removal

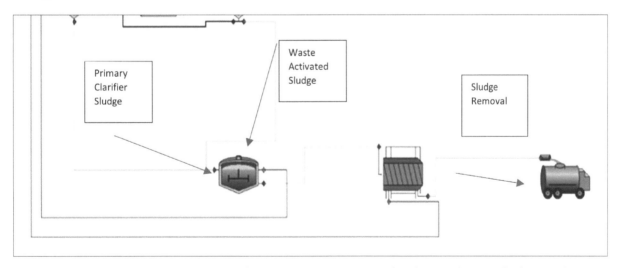

Primary Clarifier Sludge

Waste Activated Sludge

Sludge Removal

Diagram 1.3 Sludge Handling Schematic. Image courtesy of Hydromantis: www.hydromantis.com

The diagram above shows primary sludge and WAS pumped to a digester process. Generally smaller treatment plants have aerobic digesters and larger plants have anaerobic digesters. Many digesters have a stage in which mixing and/or aeration are turned off, allowing for the thickening of the digester sludge and a return side-stream decanted back into the secondary treatment process. In this instance the digester biomass is eventually sent to a belt press in which the solids are dewatered, with thick (i.e., stabilized) sludge being removed via truck and any filtrate returned to the secondary treatment process.

1.2 Mixed Liquor

Mixed liquor is measured as MLSS (mixed liquor suspended solids) and represents the available biomass for wastewater treatment. There are several main components that constitute the MLSS:

Summary of Mixed Liquor Composition

As demonstrated above, there are many complex factors that are constituted within the MLSS value. For these reasons, while MLSS is generally the best in-house application for determining biomass concentrations., it is important to note the high variability of the factors involved. Ultimately the bacteria that compete within the process will give us the best clue as to the conditions occurring within the system. MLSS concentrations and solids loading rates to clarifier(s) come into play with regard to various issues, such as clarifier performance and anticipating at what values clarifier failure may be expected.

1.2A Bacteria

Bacteria are the main "workers" in secondary treatment processes and the most essential part of the activated sludge. Wastewater treatment plants consist of a highly diverse mixture of bacteria. These contain a high potential for genetic diversity from many phyla, including Actinobacteriota, Chloroflexi, Bacteroidetes, Planctomycetota, Patescibacteria, Nitrospirota, Proteobacteria, Firmicutes, and others. The specific bacteria that will compete in aerobic wastewater treatment processes are a direct result of the substrate being treated and the conditions present within the plant.

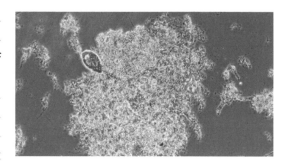

Figure 1.1 strong floc 100x phase contrast

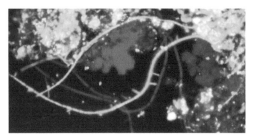

Figure 1.2 viability 1000x fluorscent

Based upon fluorescent microscopy applications, the viability of bacteria within activated sludge flocs appears to generally range between 35 and 85 percent, depending on the plant based on our experience. Good quality sludges tend to range between an estimated 40 and 75 percent viability, with viability of greater than 80 percent likely indicating high or potentially logarithmic growth rates.

1.2B Polysaccharide

Polysaccharide is produced by bacteria and plays an important role acting as the "glue" that holds flocculated bacteria together (Nielsen et al., 2003). Genera such as Zoogloea and Thauera contain thick extracellular polysaccharide capsules and when present at low to moderate abundance, are considered beneficial.

If polysaccharide becomes excessive within the flocs, other problems may develop. This is discussed in later chapters. Biopolymers and polysaccharide are together believed to make up approximately 15 to 20 percent of the MLSS by weight (Jenkins et al., 2004).

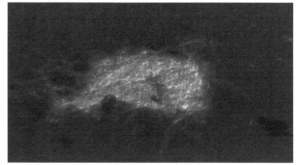

Figure 1.3 polysaccharide normal 400x

1.2C Higher Life Form Organisms

Protozoa, metazoan, and more advanced microorganisms (such as gastrotrich and tardigrades) are commonly found in secondary biological wastewater treatment processes and are believed to make up an average of 5 to 20 percent of the weight of the MLSS (Jenkins et al., 2004). However, it is possible for good treatment and good sludge quality to exist with or without the presence of higher life form organisms (Jenkins et al., 2004).

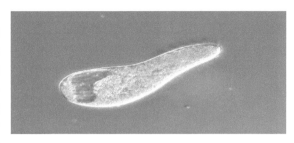

Figure 1.4 free swimming ciliate cropped from 200x DIC

While not 100 percent scientifically correct due to some exceptions, a good way to envision the role of higher life form organisms is as the "polishers" of dispersed bacteria. Bacteria are responsible for the vast majority of treatment and in general, higher life form organisms' prey on bacteria. Small amounts of other microorganisms such as fungi and yeast may also be present but contribute only a small fraction to the MLSS concentration (Jenkins et al., 2004).

1.2D Inert and Inorganic Solids

Also represented in the MLSS is a fraction of inert or inorganic solids. MLVSS (mixed liquor volatile suspended solid) is most often used to estimate the fraction of MLSS that may be inert or inorganic. Most treatment plants contain between 60 and 90 percent MLVSS as MLSS (Pennsylvania Department of Environmental Protection, 2014a). The lower the percent of MLVSS in relation to MLSS, the greater the number of inert and inorganic solids suspected to be present (Jenkins et al., 2004).

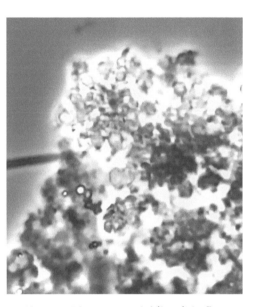

Figure 1.5 inert material (iron) in floc cropped from 1000x phase

Treatment plants that have primary treatment tend to have higher ratios of MLVSS to MLSS, as many of the inert or inorganic solids may be removed prior to entering the aeration basin. It is generally not problematic for plants to have a lesser ratio of MLVSS to MLSS, as inert solids may add weight to the flocs. However, in these instances it should be noted that the concentration of "bugs" in the system is actually less than the MLSS concentration would suggest and that higher MLSS concentrations may be needed in certain situations.

1.2E Archaea

Archaea are different from bacteria. Experience from Dr. Paul Cambell of Aster Bio suggests that the proportion of archaea to bacteria in activated sludge processes may likely range between 0.5 and 2.5 percent. In general, archaea tend to compete well in harsher environments, such as in high stress, anaerobic, thermophilic temperature ranges, high salt, or brine concentrations, et cetera.

1.3 Critical Biomass Growth Condition Parameters

The following sections detail critical growth conditions needed for selection of optimal bacteria to proliferate within the biological wastewater treatment process. General "ranges" are discussed and when conditions fall outside of these desired ranges undesirable bacteria may gain competitive advantages leading to problems that will be discussed later within this text in detail.

5

1.3A pH Impact on Wastewater Microbiology

The term "pH" represents hydrogen activity and uses a scale of 1 to 14 to represent the amount of acidity or basicity present within a water sample. A pH value of 7 is considered neutral. As the pH decreases below 7, hydrogen ions increase logarithmically as values change, whereas when pH values increase above 7, hydroxyl ions increase logarithmically.

Ideal pH Values for Aerobic Wastewater Treatment Processes

Generally, pH values between 7.0 and 8.3 appear best for aerobic biological treatment.

Should pH values fall outside of this range, a review of process and potential chemical correction may be needed to maintain critical values.

Figure 1.6 pH equipment Hach

Enzyme Functionality

For bacteria to function, conditions must be present in which their enzyme functions occur. When conditions are not conductive to enzyme function, bacteria become inhibited and are no longer able to compete (Anbu et al., 2017). Different types of bacteria have different environmental conditions in which their enzymes are active. It is widely accepted that causes of toxicity and inhibition are related to the crippling of bacterial enzyme activity. Should conditions change in which desirable bacterial enzymes may not function, other potentially non-desirable bacteria whose enzymes function well in the new environment may then proliferate. Bacteria produce their own enzymes naturally (Snyder and Wyant, n.d.).

1.3B Alkalinity

Alkalinity is a measurement of the extent to which water resists a decrease in pH (Utah State University Extension, n.d.). A good way to envision alkalinity is the "buffering capacity" to resist acidification. Alkalinity is oftentimes associated with basicity; however, this is incorrect due to exceptions such as CO_2, which may depress pH while leaving alkalinity unchanged. The science of alkalinity and its relationship to biochemical reactions is relatively complex. However, from an operational and practical viewpoint, viewing alkalinity as a "buffering capacity" to resist changes in pH is recommended.

Testing Methods and Recommended Residual Concentrations

Without going too deeply into chemistry, the predominant components of alkalinity are bicarbonate, carbonate, and hydroxide. Alkalinity may be tested for using methods such as titration, colorimetric testing, and test strips.

Dr. Michael Richard recommends testing residual alkalinity in the filtered mixed liquor or biomass prior to the clarifier (or other liquids-solids separation step) once biological treatment is completed to **ensure a total alkalinity residual of >100 mg/L at all times** (Richard, 2003). The reason for testing alkalinity prior to the clarifier is that alkalinity is recovered or increased in certain processes such as denitrification, which may occur in final clarifiers and thus artificially increase the total alkalinity residual reading.

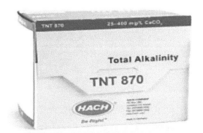

Figure 1.7 Alkalinity test

Biological Processes in Wastewater Treatment in Which Alkalinity is Critical

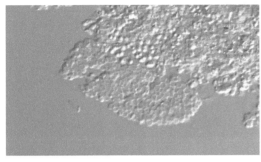

Figure 1.8 Nitrosomonas 1000x DIC cropped

As discussed above, should the pH value fall below 7, negative impacts on the wastewater microbiology, associated with the crippling of bacteria enzyme functionality, increase. Measuring alkalinity is often advantageous for preventing a pH decrease from occurring—a proactive rather than reactive approach. As alkalinity concentrations begin to fall below 50 mg/L, the depression of pH values begins to occur. It is thus important to be aware of the following biological processes in wastewater in which alkalinity is consumed:

Nitrification

High amounts of alkalinity are consumed for nitrification. During nitrification, 7.14 mg of alkalinity as CaCO3 is destroyed for every milligram of ammonium ion oxidized (Evans & Sober, n.d.). Alkalinity thus acts as the "food" for nitrifying bacteria. If carbonate alkalinity is lacking, nitrification will cease. In denitrification processes, approximately one-half of the alkalinity lost through nitrification is recovered.

Fermentation Reactions

When free dissolved oxygen and combined oxygen sources are depleted, acid-forming bacteria reduce organic matter into organic acids. If alkalinity values are limited, the formation of these organic acids may depress the pH value. Alkalinity monitoring is especially essential in designated anaerobic digestion processes and acid to alkalinity ratios of 0.1-0.25 are recommended (Wisconsin Department of Natural Resources Bureau of Science Services, 1992a). If alkalinity becomes limited in anaerobic digestion processes, the pH values may decrease, ceasing the activity of methane-producing bacteria. This event is often called a "sour" or "stuck" anaerobic digester (Wisconsin Department of Natural Resources Bureau of Science Services, 1992b).

Chemical Addition of Iron or Aluminum Salts

Chemicals such as ferric sulfate, ferric chloride, ferrous sulfate, ferrous chloride, or aluminum sulfate (also known as alum), which are often used for processes such as chemical phosphorous removal, consume alkalinity and, in many instances, may require close attention to alkalinity values to prevent the depression of pH. Additional supplementation chemicals include calcium oxide or calcium hydroxide (lime); magnesium hydroxide or magnesium bicarbonate; sodium hydroxide (caustic soda); and sodium carbonate (soda ash) or sodium bicarbonate (Trygar, May 2014).

1.3C Time (Sludge Retention Time and Hydraulic Retention Time)

In most biological treatment processes the hydraulic retention time (HRT)—the theoretical time the flow stays in the plant—is separate from the sludge retention time—the theoretical time a "microbe" stays in the system. The biochemical reactions needed for "treatment" (or carbonaceous BOD removal) commonly occur within 3–4 hours, while the sludge biomass must be maintained to meet the growth rates of the desired microorganisms at the desired concentrations for treatment. Nitrification commonly takes between 6 to 15 hours (Pennsylvania Department of Environmental Protection, 2014b).

Sludge Retention Time (SRT)

The separation of HRT and SRT is commonly accomplished through return activated sludge (RAS) flow in which each "microbe" makes up to several passes through the aeration basin and settles out in the clarifier each day, eventually either wasted (WAS) or lost to the effluent. Another common method of separating HRT from SRT is fixed film processes in which bacteria grow on media staying in a tank until they eventually slough off. SRT values for fixed film processes are difficult if not impossible to theoretically calculate, while SRT values in conventional treatment plants are generally 5–15 days, and 15–30 days or longer in extended aeration processes (Wisconsin Department of Natural Resources Bureau of Science Services, 2010).

SRT values become essential for maintaining adequate populations of more slowly growing bacteria, such as nitrifying bacteria, should nitrification be desired.

Calculating SRT

There are several methods for calculating SRT. Be aware that SRT can commonly appear interchangeable with the categories of "Mean Cell Residence Time" (MCRT) and "Sludge Age" (Trygar, 2014, June). The most important factor for SRT is that whatever method is being used for calculation is consistent and also that the calculation may be described accurately to engineers, consultants, or anyone else who may request this information.

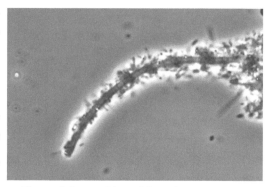

Figure 1.9 type 0041_0675 phase contrast cropped 1000x

All calculations of SRT involve dividing the overall mass of estimated "microbes" in the system per day by the mass of estimated "microbes" that leaves the system per day. Some plants include calculating the mass of solids in the final clarifier(s). This is generally considered good practice, especially if the sludge blankets hold an adequate percentage of the biomass at any given time. In plants where the sludge blanket in the final clarifier(s) is minimal, common practice generally elects to use the mass of solids in the aeration basin and any selector zones, applying the MLSS concentration in this calculation for practical application. Calculating the mass of solids leaving the system is generally accomplished through the WAS rate. However, if effluent suspended solids are significant, it may be wise to also include these in the calculation as solids leaving the system per day.

SRT Calculation Example. If the aeration basin holds 1 million gallons (1 MG) and the MLSS concentration is 3500 mg/L, the total lbs. of solids in the aeration basin may be calculated as:

1MG * 8.34 lbs./gallon * 3500 mg/L = 21,190 lbs.

The WAS concentration of the solids is 8000 mg/L, and 50,000 gallons of WAS are sent to a digester. The number of solids removed from the system is calculated as:

8,000 mg/L * 0.05 MG * 8.34= 3,336 lbs.

To calculate the SRT value the total lbs. of solids inventory are then divided by the lbs. of solids leaving the system per day.

*21,190 lbs. solids inventory / 3,336 lbs. solids leaving per day = **6.35 days***

Operational Strategy: SRT versus Constant MLSS

In personal experience, values such as SRT and MLSS concentrations should ideally be monitored and used in combination with microscopy evaluations to determine wasting rates. The general philosophy is to obtain as consistent of an SRT value as possible while letting the MLSS drift between pre-determined values (i.e., between 3,500 and 4,500 mg/L) based on plant specific targets in regard to other parameters, such as the clarifier solids loading rate, hydraulic flow rates, and sludge volume index (SVI) values. Using this general approach, the target wasting rate using SRT generally remains constant, unless the MLSS concentration drifts outside of the targeted range. As with just about everything in wastewater treatment there are always exceptions and in certain instances other factors take precedence.

While the theoretical mathematical values obtained through calculation are important, other factors such as sudden changes to the sludge settling characteristics and changes observed through microscopy should not be ignored. Ultimately, "the bugs do not lie," and the bacteria that compete in the treatment process are a direct result of the substrate utilized ("you are what you eat") and the conditions in which the bacteria are exposed. The added value of using microscopy to assist with operational control decisions is dependent on the accuracy and interpretation of microscopy findings, in combination with a smart understanding of when to make changes to the system and what these changes should be.

An often-overlooked factor among consultants for operational process control decisions is the individual hands-on practical experience of operational personnel. A high number of samples that I evaluate are to help confirm what operational staff believes is happening and to justify recommended changes, and in most instances their "gut" feeling is correct. As a former operator with over 15 years of hands-on experience I developed a very good "feel" over time for how the plant I was operating would likely respond to various changes. I never personally recommend any operational changes without talking to operational staff and gathering an understanding of factors such as urgency, cost logistics, permit limits, and so forth.

Understanding the Bacterial Growth Curve and Why Not to Chase the MLSS Concentration

The concept of constant SRT values is intended to help maintain consistent bacterial growth rates. As a result of aerobic biological treatment approximately 1 lb. of BOD is converted into 0.5 lbs. of new "bugs, "so when there are significant increases in the influent loading rates, increases in the MLSS concentration generally occur (Pennsylvania Department of Environmental Protection, 2014a). When the WAS rate is increased as an initial reaction to seeing an increase in the MLSS concentration, this has the potential to further increase the growth rates and oxygen uptake rates of the bacteria if the organic loading rate remains elevated. A good way to understand this principle is to visualize the bacteria as always trying to obtain the MLSS concentration that they want, based on the loading rate. The more available food present in proportion to viable microorganisms, the higher the growth rates, and many of the microorganisms that are undesirable at high abundance, such as zoogloea, many types of filaments, and so on, favor high bacterial growth rates.

While it may appear counterintuitive, many plants have success decreasing the WAS rate when they know that there is a high incoming organic load. Then, once things have stabilized, they increase the WAS rate slightly to slowly reduce the MLSS concentration back to target concentrations. Wasting aggressively during periods of high loading creates higher growth rates and the likelihood of undesirable bacteria proliferating within the treatment plant. Changes are case specific. Generally, a good operator develops a good intuition over time for using the information available as a reference.

An example from personal experience at an industrial wastewater treatment plant that treated very high strength waste (an average of 2500 mg/L BOD) was that if a "spill" occurred, which could then increase incoming BOD values to over 6,000 mg/L, the flow rate needed to be slowed down considerably from the EQ tank to prevent the bacteria from entering logarithmic growth stages. In some instances, if the flow was not decreased in time to help maintain the relative loading rate in terms of pounds of BOD, the growth rates and oxygen uptake rates of the bacteria would surpass the available aeration capacity. When this occurred on occasion, the flow would need to be completely stopped, sometimes for up to several hours, before the DO again returned to desired values, which in this instance was a target of 2.5 mg/L DO.

During these periods of logarithmic bacteria growth, there was essentially no value to wasting, as wasting only served to further increase the F/M ratio and the bacterial growth rates. This particular plant had the luxury of the EQ tank for buffering capacity. However, not all plants have these capabilities. In many of these scenarios as operators, we are at the mercy of what comes down to the treatment plant and can only act accordingly. Wastewater treatment is one of the few processes where we are tasked with controlling the final product, but sometimes have little influence on the characteristics of the incoming factors.

Hydraulic Retention Time (HRT)

Hydraulic retention time (HRT) is a calculation of the estimated time water stays within a particular area. Treatment plants with equalization tanks or upstream anaerobic processes may have a limited amount of flexibility for increasing or decreasing the flow rate to the downstream aerobic biological treatment process, while for many plants the HRT is defined exclusively by the incoming flow rates. HRT becomes especially important in instances such as rain or other high flow events in municipal treatment plants due to factors such as inflow and infiltration (also referred to as "I and I"). As the hydraulic flow rates increase and the HRT in the final clarifier(s) decreases, eventually clarifier failure may occur in which the bacteria either do not have enough time to settle out, or the sludge simply cannot be removed from the clarifier(s) faster than the rate that sludge is accumulating in the clarifier(s). Clarifier performance may be estimated using control tools such as state point analysis. (Wastewater Blog, 2017). Basically, in relation to HRT, each plant may have a slightly different point in which precative measures are needed. This is a major part of what distinguishes "conditions" from "problems."

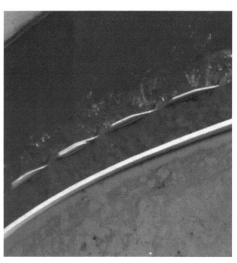

Figure 1.10 sludge bulking TSS carryover

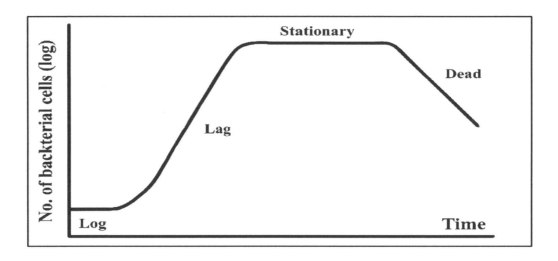

Diagram 1.4 Bacterial Growth Curve (Wang et al., 2015).

Diagram 1.4 shows the bacterial growth curve. Generally, in successful wastewater treatment processes the system operates in the very end of the stationary phase, even a little into the endogenous (or death and starvation) phase, with a minimal peak of growth rate at the front end of the aeration basin when substrate and oxygen demand is the highest. When growth rates and corresponding oxygen uptake rates increase above 60 mg/L/hr. dispersed bacteria growth becomes probable (Richard, 2003).

Measuring HRT

When referencing HRT values, it is important to clearly define the area which the measurement is related to. For example, HRT could be looked at for the time the water spends in the primary clarifier, selector zones, the aeration basin, or the entire duration of treatment. In most conventional activated sludge treatment plants, the theoretical time a drop of water remains in the plant generally ranges between 4 and 18 hours

(Calculating the Hydraulic Retention Time, 2021). Within 4 hours and at the proper conditions, especially having enough bacteria available for treatment, most biochemical reactions are completed. However, this is very dependent on the type of waste being treated, and the more complex the organic material, the more time needed for enzyme activity to "break" the substrate down to make it available for the bacteria and ultimately for "treatment".

In wastewater treatment the proper time and numbers are needed in order to treat the incoming organic loading rate successfully. Most commonly, the "bottleneck" in regard to HRT is the final clarifier performance capacity. To present an HRT measurement example:

If a plant's aeration basin volume is 1 MG (million gallon) and the HRT is 1200 gallons per minute (gpm), multiply the HRT by the minutes per hour to get the total gallons per hour (gph):

*1200 gpm * 60 minutes / hr. = 72,000 gph*

Then divide the aeration basin volume by the gph to get the amount of time in hours:

1,000,000 gallons / 72,000 gallons / hr. = **13.89 hours**

1.3D Temperature

In general, as temperatures in the aeration basin increase there is a corresponding increase in the rate of the metabolic processes and biochemical reactions of the bacteria. For this reason, with seasonal temperature fluctuation, it is common in municipal treatment processes to require higher MLSS concentrations during the winter months than the summer months. For example, in Wisconsin it is common for a municipal treatment plant to operate at 2,500 mg/L MLSS in the summer while concentrations of around 3,500 mg/L may be needed in the coldest months of the winter to maintain the same degree of treatment at the same loading rates.

Temperature Ranges

Bacteria may be roughly classified into different temperature ranges, depending on the ranges in which their enzymes are able to function. When temperatures fall outside of the functional ranges for the bacteria, they become inhibited and other bacteria (or archaea) that compete in the new temperature range then become predominant (Lumen, n.d.). The following provides the functional temperature ranges for bacteria:

Psychrotrophic Bacteria. Microorganisms categorized as psychotrophs function between approximately 4°C and 25°C (39°F–68°F).

Mesophilic Bacteria. Microorganisms categorized as mesophiles are adapted to moderate temperatures, with optimal growth temperatures ranging from 20°C to approximately 40 °C (68°F–104°F).

Thermophilic Bacteria. Thermophilic bacteria exist at temperatures above 40°C (104°F).

Crossing through Temperature Ranges

Aerobic biological wastewater treatment processes generally function within the psychotropic and mesophilic temperature ranges. In certain industrial wastewater treatment processes, problems may develop when the temperature in the aeration basin crosses to the thermophilic from the mesophilic temperature range. Basically, once the temperature reaches the thermophilic range, the mesophilic bacteria are no longer able to function, and rapid growth of thermophilic bacteria occurs. Treatment may be obtained in the thermophilic range; however, these processes are rare and often not cost effective due to limited oxygen solubility at higher temperatures. It is best practice to avoid crossing between the mesophilic and thermophilic temperature ranges.

1.3E Dissolved Oxygen (DO)

Overview

For aerobic biochemical reactions to occur, free dissolved oxygen (DO) must be the terminal electron acceptor involved. A good way to envision DO readings obtained from inline meters or handheld probes is that these devices are reading "residual" DO outside of the biological flocs. DO depletion will occur through the floc, so the higher the oxygen uptake rate of the bacteria the more DO needed to maintain aerobic conditions within the floc. In most municipal treatment processes, 2–3 mg/L of DO is adequate to maintain aerobic conditions within the floc at the initial contact zone of the aeration basin when the bacterial oxygen demand is the highest. However, in some instances, when there are higher initial oxygen uptake rates, higher DO setpoints may be needed to discourage the growth of low DO filaments.

Figure 1.10 Hach DO probe

Actual DO Demand

A good example of varying DO setpoints may be systems such as Unox (pure oxygen) systems, designed for a very high initial F/M ratio and a small overall footprint (Richard, 1993; Veolia, n.d.). In many Unox processes or treatment plants that treat high concentrations of organic acid substrate, DO setpoints above 5 mg/L may be needed to prevent the proliferation of low DO filaments. A particular Unox system we work with needs a DO setpoint of generally >8 mg/L to discourage low DO filaments. I also worked for many years at a municipal wastewater treatment system that treated approximately 35 percent loading of paper mill wastewater, containing high organic acids and high BOD concentrations. Typically, when the DO setpoint was below 4 mg/L, low DO filaments would proliferate. On the other end of the spectrum, I have conducted microscopy analysis for a handful of lightly loaded municipal treatment plants in which the DO setpoint is only 1 mg/L but fully nitrified; they do not have troubles with low DO filaments. In summary, the term "low DO" is relative to the amount of oxygen that the bacteria actually need (Richard, 1993).

Ideally, inline DO meters should be placed near the front end of the aeration basin where the DO demand for bacteria is the highest (YSI, n.d.). Some plants with a plug flow configuration have obtained significant energy savings by tapering down the DO supply to match the demand as the oxygen demand decreases along the aeration basin. These energy-saving processes are generally successful, provided that there is enough DO and low enough oxygen uptake rates entering the final clarifier(s) to discourage denitrification. Should nitrification occur in the aeration basin, it can be maintained if desired, as long as low DO filaments do not proliferate and cause settling problems. For plants that are working to optimize energy costs associated with aeration, microscopy with an emphasis on the abundance of low DO filaments may often be a useful operational tool.

Complete Mix Systems

For aeration basins with complete mix configuration, the DO demand and oxygen uptake rate of the bacteria should theoretically be consistent in all areas of the basin. In these processes, the placement of inline DO probes should be relatively insignificant as DO measurements should be the same throughout the basin.

Anoxic Reactions

Most bacteria selected in wastewater treatment processes are facultative, meaning that when free DO is not present, the bacteria may utilize the oxygen combined in forms such as nitrate and sulfate. Anoxic reactions produce similar biomass yields as aerobic reactions and oxidize organic material, producing byproducts such as nitrogen gas (denitrification) or sulfide (if sulfate is reduced) (Kelly et al., 2001). The order of anoxic reactions begins with nitrate and when all nitrate is utilized, sulfate becomes the next combined oxygen source. Once sulfate is depleted, fermentation reactions occur in which longer chained organic compounds are broken down into simpler, more readily available substrate. Additional information on this topic is available in the low DO filament section of the book.

1.3F Nutrients

Generally, a theoretical BOD:N:P value of 100:5:1 provides adequate macronutrients for bacteria. Using this nutrient ratio, an estimated mass balance of nutrients may be obtained. For example, a plant takes the following measurements:

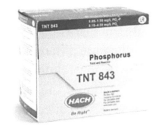

Influent BOD: 200 mg/L

Influent TKN: 25 mg/L

Influent Total P: 5 mg/L

Figure 1.12 Hach phosphorous test

Using the 100:5:1 ratio and assuming all phosphorous and TKN becomes available (i.e., ammonia and orthophosphate) approximately 10 mg/L TKN-nitrogen and approximately 2 mg/L phosphorous would then be assimilated into new cell mass. This leaves behind 15 mg/L of nitrogen and 3 mg/L of phosphorous. Residual ammonia nitrogen beyond what is utilized for cellular nutrients is then subject to nitrification (oxidation to nitrite and then nitrate), and the 3 mg/L of residual phosphorous would pass through into the effluent or be subjected to chemical removal should a phosphorus limit be in place.

Practical Application

The actual nutrient requirements needed for aerobic treatment are often less than mathematical projected values, depending on factors such as the internal recycling of nutrients within the system. For example, systems that operate at higher SRT values or higher temperatures (with accompanying higher metabolic rates of bacteria), nutrients may be re-released through endogenous activity and cell lysis (Jenkins et al., 2004). Additionally, other systems such as Aerated Stabilization Basins (ASBs) and lagoon processes have the potential for benthic feedback, in which nutrients may be re-released from settled sludge to provide another form of internal nutrient recycling. Side-stream processes, such as sludge handling return side streams, are also commonly high in phosphorous and ammonia.

Macronutrient Residuals

In addition to paying attention to the nutrient mass balance characteristics of the influent, nutrient supplementation may be optimized through monitoring residual total inorganic nitrogen (TIN) and orthophosphate in the filtered mixed liquor or biomass at the end of treatment, prior to the clarifier(s). TIN (ammonia + nitrite + nitrate) residuals of >1 mg/L and orthophosphate residuals of >1 mg/L are commonly obtained to ensure adequate nutrients are available. Should nutrient residuals increase above pre-determined setpoints, nutrient supplementation may be reduced. In general, the higher the variability of the BOD:N:P ratio, the higher a "safety factor/residual" value is needed.

Macronutrient Supplementation

It is extremely rare for nutrients to be limited in municipal treatment processes that treat predominantly domestic wastewater while certain wastewater treatment influents may require constant nutrient supplementation. The impact of nutrients is described in greater detail in the problems and troubleshooting section of this textbook, and their mention here serves only as a general introduction.

The following growth factors also have high contribution potential for the selection of which bacteria will grow within the treatment plant.

1.3G Fats, Oils, and Grease (FOG) Concentrations

Certain bacteria, as well as filamentous bacteria morphotypes including Microthrix and Actinomycetes-Mycolata may utilize lipids or long chain fatty acids which are formed when FOG becomes septic allowing bacteria to ferment this substrate allowing it to be more readily available for filamentous bacteria.

1.3H Composition of Wastewater (Other)

A major factor in the selection of bacteria that proliferate within the treatment plant system is simply the type of substrate present (you are what you eat). Composition of municipal-residential treatment plants may be significantly different from various industrial treatment processes and the bacteria observed in these instances are largely related to the composition of the wastewater. Additionally, the higher the concentration of organic material of the wastewater, the greater the chance of septicity occurring prior to the treatment plant (i.e. eq basins, collection systems). The concentration of organic acids is a major factor for selection of bacteria that compete in wastewater treatment systems.

Salinity plays a major role in selection of bacteria. Challenges with high salinity include the potential for an elevated mono-divalent cation ratio (to be discussed in later chapters of this text) which may contribute to dispersed growth. Additionally, bacterial enzyme function may be highly impacted by salinity levels. Bacteria that are acclimated to high salinity may eventually compete (for example similar biochemical reactions for natural biological treatment of organic materials occur in the oceans). Major variations in salinity concentrations are undesirable for stable biological wastewater treatment and may often pose challenges when saltwater inflow and infiltration occur in coastal treatment plants.

C1 compounds (single-carbon molecules such as methanol) are significant for the growth of many types of bacteria that may proliferate in wastewater treatment systems. An example of this is Hyphomicrobium, a small, thin, typically non-bulking microbe type. Generally, microbe types such as Hyphomicrobium do not pose challenges but are rather indicators that C1 compounds are present in the wastewater being treated. C1 compounds are a natural byproduct of many industrial treatment processes or may be formed in areas of deep septicity/fermentation.

Inhibition and stress may often play a significant role in which bacteria are able to compete. The mixed liquor population is highly competitive and any time a certain type of bacteria loses its competitive advantage, the void is quickly filled with new bacteria. Depending on the amount, type, and frequency of any inhibition within the system this may greatly impact the microbiology of the population.

Finally, chemical additives may play a factor in competition. For example, if ferric chloride is added for phosphorous removal, it is likely that iron oxidizing bacteria will gain a competitive advantage. While the population of these types of microorganisms is generally low/fairly insignificant, it is still worth noting in this text.

Chapter 2:

Common Problems Encountered in Biological Treatment Processes

2.1 Filamentous Bulking Defined

In most biological wastewater treatment processes, the final step of separating biosolids from treated effluent requires the sludge to settle adequately within the final clarifier(s). Sludge Volume Index (SVI) is a measurement in which the MLSS concentration is compared to the 30-minute settling characteristics of the sludge (SV30) or biomass. In most processes, SVI values between 50 and 150 mL/g are considered acceptable (Trygar, 2010).

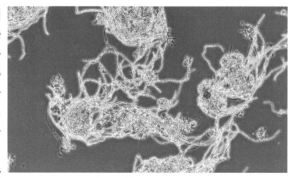

Figure 2.1 abundant filaments 100x phase contrast

SVI is calculated by dividing the MLSS concentration by the 30-minute settling volume (SV30) and then multiplying by 100.

> **Example #1:** A plant's measurements are SV30 = 200 mL and an MLSS concentration of 2000 mg/L.
>
> *200 / 2000 = 0.1*
>
> *0.1*100 =* **100 mL/g**

> **Example #2:** A plant's measurements are SV30 = 400 mL and an MLSS concentration of 2000 mg/L.
>
> *400 / 2000 = 0.2*
>
> *0.2*100 =* **200 mL/g**

Per observation, the higher the SVI value, the less compactable the mixed liquor or sludge settlement is. Note that the SVI values of concern are site specific, with a large emphasis on hydraulic flow rates and clarifier surface area.

2.1A State Point Analysis Considerations

The MLSS concentrations and SVI values in which clarifier failure occurs, leading to a loss of suspended solids, is site specific. A "worst case scenario" may be achieved through state point analysis calculations, which provide a clarifier performance forecast by inputting theoretical numbers in the spreadsheet for influent flow, SVI, MLSS concentration, RAS rate, and the surface area of clarifier(s). Information on state point analysis as well as a downloadable pre-filled excel sheet can easily be found on a quick internet search (O&M News, 2003; Wastewater Blog, 2017).

My personal experience with state point analysis has revealed additional factors for consideration, such as the following:

- In periods of high hydraulic loading events, solids will migrate or shift to the clarifier(s). As this occurs, the MLSS concentration and potentially the solids loading rate to the clarifier(s) may decrease.

- In practical applications for high flow events, we have found state point analysis useful for determining at what parameters clarifier failure is expected. This can be used as a good benchmark to determine when operational changes should be made in preparation for higher flow rates.

- State point analysis calculations will always suggest that a lower MLSS concentration will improve SVI while this is not always the case. Significantly changing the MLSS concentration has the potential to significantly impact the types of bacteria that will compete in the process as well as raise the F/M ratio should organic loading rates remain constant which does not always lead to an improvement in settling.
    - In practice, we have encountered many scenarios in which a higher MLSS concentration produces a lower SV30 settling volume.

2.2 Diffuse Floc Structure versus Filaments Extending or Bridging Flocs Together

There are two common ways in which filamentous bulking can occur:

2.2A Diffuse Floc Structure

Bulking due to diffuse floc structure generally occurs when filaments are predominantly located within the floc, as this creates open or void spaces. In these events, the mass of the floc is compromised and settling rates decrease due to less gravitational pull on the mass of the floc structure.

Figure 2.2 diffuse flocs 100x

2.2B Filaments Extending from the Flocs and/or Bridging Flocs Together

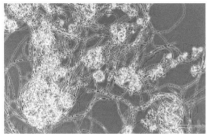

Figure 2.3 bridging 100x

Often in these instances the overall floc structure may be firm. However, filamentous bacteria interfere with the settling or compacting characteristics of the sludge, as filaments extend from the flocs or bridge flocs together. A good way to envision this is to think of the filaments as a direct barrier that prevents flocs from compacting on top of each other. Because filaments are between the separate flocs, the overall compaction for settleability is reduced and therefore the volume in which the sludge compacts or settles is increased.

2.3 Slime Bulking Defined

"Slime bulking" differentiates from filamentous bulking in that rather than filamentous bacteria deemed responsible for elevated SVI values, the formation of excess polysaccharide—given the term "slime" due to its viscous properties—is diagnosed as the root cause.

2.3A Types of Slime Bulking

Zoogloeal Bacteria Type Bulking

In these events, zoogloeal bacteria types proliferate in the mixed liquor. Zoogloea bacteria morphological traits include a thick polysaccharide or "slime" capsule. Excess zoogloeal bacteria often negatively impact settling characteristics in the following ways:

- A viscous floc structure is typically the most common.

Figure 2.4 400x DIC elevated polysaccharide zoogloea

- Polysaccharide within the floc becomes elevated and creates viscous flocs in which the floc structure becomes less strong or compact, slowing down the settling properties of the sludge.

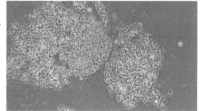

Figure 2.5 viscous flocs 100x phase

- In addition to the compromised floc structure, polysaccharide is also hydrophobic in nature, so there is an upward force that results in flotation, versus the gravitational force normally exerted on the flocs that causes settling to occur.

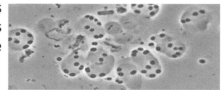

Figure 2.6 bacteria with elevated polysaccharide 1000x phase

True Slime Bulking

In instances of true slime bulking, polysaccharide acts like filamentous bacteria extending from the flocs by which the presence of excess polysaccharide forms layers between the flocs, inhibiting the ability of the sludge to compact well.

In practice, these events appear to be less common. However, if present, the settling properties of the sludge appear to be extremely poor and there is often accompanying polysaccharide foam or scum.

Figure 2.7 Anthrone test in progress

Slime Bulking Due to Nutrient Deficiency

When nutrients are limited, bacterial growth is shunted to the formation of exocellular polysaccharide rather than the production of new biomass (Jenkins et al., 2004). As polysaccharide increases within the flocs, bulking may occur in the same manner as described above.

Anthrone testing is a commonly used tool to differentiate between excess polysaccharide attributed to zoogloeal bacteria types and polysaccharide attributed to low nutrient availability conditions. The carbohydrates attributed to zoogloeal bacteria types do not react in this testing procedure (Jenkins et al., 2004). In general, if polysaccharide per dry weight of the biomass is >20–25% per Anthrone test, low nutrient availability is suspected (Jenkins et al., 2004).

2.4 Pin Floc Defined

Pin floc are classified as floc that have a dimension of <50μm. Pin flocs are much smaller than average flocs observed in activated sludge processes. Pin floc may either settle rapidly, often leaving behind a turbid supernatant layer above the settled sludge, or in other instances can create a "pinball" effect in which flocs repel against each other. This latter state can result in an elevated SVI value.

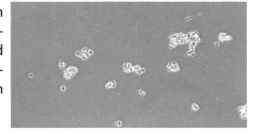
Figure 2.8 pin floc 100x phase

2.4A Pin Floc Causes

There are two main causes for pin floc. Note, that it may often be challenging to differentiate causes of pin floc through microscopy observations. There are instances in which the two causes for pin floc, as defined below, may occur simultaneously. When pin floc diagnosis is difficult through microscopy, additional tools such as DNA sequencing and operational analytical data are recommended. The two main causes for pin floc are:

Chronic Stress

Chronic stress within the system is a common (and often overlooked) cause for the proliferation of pin floc. While the biochemistry reactions remain somewhat poorly understood at this time, the accepted theory is that chronic system stress may interfere with the biopolymer or flocculating properties of the bacteria.

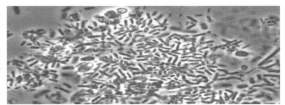
Figure 2.9 irregular growth formations cropped from 1000x

Examples of potential chronic stress include the following:

- A pH consistently maintained below 7.
- Elevated concentrations of low molecular weight organic acids (Berg, et al., 2002, section 22.3).

- Odd-numbered carbon organic acids (i.e., propionic acid) are suspected to cause inhibition at threshold concentrations. At the time of this writing there is no clear literature to reference specific concentrations where problems are likely to develop.

- Chronic low dissolved oxygen concentrations.

- Inhibition or toxicity-related events.

Endogeny or Starvation Conditions

If the sludge becomes "burned out" in which there is no remaining available substrate, the bacteria begin endogenous functions (i.e., "cannibalism"). These instances can occur at excessively high SRT (sludge retention time) values and/or if a large portion of the treatment plant lacks available substrate for the bacteria.

In general, the progression of pin floc through endogenous conditions undergoes a series of events in which high SRT filamentous bacteria initially emerge; eventually, when the F/M gets too low for even these filaments to compete, the flocs become "skeleton-like."

Pin floc attributed to endogeny, or starvation processes does not occur overnight. Such conditions generally take at least a week or longer to develop, based on our experience. Once endogenous conditions develop, we suspect that the bacteria which consume polysaccharide as substrate (i.e., members the Patescibacteria phylum) emerge and consume polysaccharide, the "glue" that holds the flocs together. This eventually creates pin floc.

2.5 Denitrification Defined

Denitrification is simply defined as a biochemical reaction in which nitrate is converted to nitrogen gas through the oxidation of a carbon source. For denitrification to occur, the following three variables are needed (Cooke, nd):

- Anoxic conditions, in which no free dissolved oxygen is present.

- The presence of nitrate.

- The presence of a carbon source, usually a soluble carbonaceous material or substrate that is internally stored by the bacteria.

Figure 2.10 denitrification/ rising sludge

2.5A Denitrification Impacts on Treatment Performance and Settling

Floating Sludge

Once free dissolved oxygen is depleted, the bacteria will then utilize nitrate (a combined oxygen source) for respiration. When nitrate is utilized by the bacteria, they produce nitrogen gas.

Secondary clarifiers can typically avoid sludge flotation when influent nitrate is below 10 mg/L but not when it is over 10 mg/L because of the effect of hydrostatic pressure keeping the dissolved nitrogen gas from forming gas bubbles. This is one reason to accomplish some denitrification in the bioreactor prior to the clarifier(s) (The Engineering Toolbox, 2018).

Note that nitrogen gas is not water soluble and will escape into the atmosphere. If nitrogen gas becomes trapped within the biological flocs, the gas can float the flocs causing a foam or scum. This scum typically appears on the clarifier surface and occasionally in anoxic zones or aeration basins in which the floc interiors are anoxic. Activated sludge processes with higher filamentous bacteria abundance are generally more susceptible to denitrification due to the added ability to trap nitrogen gas (Jenkins et al., 2004).

From an operational standpoint, floating sludge or denitrification often poses an issue when the solids float beyond the clarifier baffle into the effluent, creating an elevated level of total suspended solids.

Nitrogen Gas Entrapment Impact on SVI

In our experience, a somewhat common but often overlooked problem is nitrogen gas entrapment within the flocs as a cause of elevated SVI values. In these instances, the interior of the flocs become anoxic and nitrogen gas is formed and trapped within the floc, creating a situation in which the gravitational settling characteristics of the floc are resisted by the upward force of nitrogen gas wanting to float the flocs to the surface.

A test we call the "paddle test," invented by Dr. Michael Richard, can be performed to determine if nitrogen gas entrapment is impacting floc settling characteristics. This test simply puts two 30-minute settlometer tests side by side, with one test receiving normal or minimal mixing and the other test mixed vigorously with a paddle for 2–3 minutes, to drive out any entrapped nitrogen gas. If the 30-minute settling test with the additional mixing settles significantly better than the other test, this implicates nitrogen gas entrapment as a cause for elevated SVI value.

Hindered Settling Disclaimer

In our experience, hindered settling is one of the more challenging issues to address. In most instances the root cause of these issues is poor floc formation. The diluted settleability test will usually demonstrate that a lesser mixed liquor concentration may improve settleability. However, this does not show the whole picture.

The flaw in the diluted settleability test is that at lesser MLSS concentrations, the test does not account for how a significant change in the F/M ratio will impact the microbiology. For example, the floc structure and microorganisms selected may be vastly different at lesser MLSS, and a lower MLSS concentration does not always equate to a lower SV30 volume. A strong case can be made to disregard any diluted settleability tests and rather rely on accurate microscopy and analytical testing information to determine if a lower a MLSS concentration may be warranted.

2.6 Dispersed Growth Defined

Dispersed growth can be defined as biological growth that occurs in the bulk liquid between the flocs, rather than within the floc structure. Dispersed growth may often contribute to turbidity in the supernatant layer above the settled mixed liquor should the flocs settle quickly enough to leave these microorganisms behind.

Types of dispersed growth include the following:

- Dispersed single cell bacteria

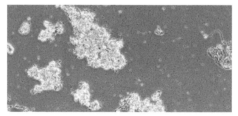

Figure 2.11 dispersed single cell 100x phase

- Dispersed "fines" or dead cellular material

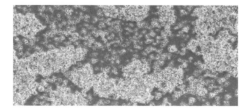

Figure 2.12 dispersed dead cellular material 100x phase

- Dispersed filamentous bacteria

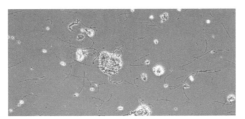

Figure 2.13 dispersed filaments 100x phase

2.6A Dispersed Single Cell Bacteria Causes

High Bacterial Growth Rates in the Initial Contact Zone of the Aeration Basin

Generally, at oxygen uptake rates of >60 mg/L/hr., dispersed single cell bacteria may gain a competitive advantage over floc-forming bacteria.

Elevated Concentrations of Low Molecular Weight Organic Acids and a High Percentage of Readily Available Substrate

This cause is like the above but can be overlooked if an elaboration of the F/M (food-to-microorganism) ratio is lacking. Note that all "BOD" is not created equally. To understand this concept, picture the impact of eating oatmeal vs. drinking Kool-Aid—the former has a high glycemic index value and takes your stomach a long time to metabolize, while the latter is full of sugar that is rapidly metabolized. Particulate BOD is adsorbed onto the surface of the flocs and broken down through enzyme activity to eventually penetrate the cell membrane of the bacteria. In contrast, soluble BOD—think "smaller pieces"— enters the metabolic process of bacteria more rapidly. Note that when fermentation reactions occur, rather than producing new biomass as the predominant end product, substrate is instead reduced to more readily available forms (organic acids).

Shock Load

A "shock load" occurs when there is a radical change to the type of food or substrate that the bacteria are acclimated to. Examples of shock loads include:

- An immediate charge in production by upstream processes that generates wastewater.
- The addition of a new waste-stream that encompasses a significant percentage of the overall flow.
- An immediate change in chemical composition of wastewater such as:
  o pH
  o Salinity
  o Temperature
  o Others (various)

Slug Load

Slug loads occur when the BOD concentration of the influent increases significantly. Slug loads often cause dispersed growth or other changes in microbial characteristics due to increased bacterial growth rates and the additional impact these changes may cause. Changes include but are not limited to a blower capacity that may be exceeded, pH levels that may drop, or nutrients that may become limited if they are not supplemented accordingly in certain instances to match the BOD:N:P ratio.

In practical application, it appears that the BOD concentrations are often a more significant factor than the overall lbs./day BOD loading rate in slug load events.

Cation Imbalance

Without going into great technical detail, simply put there are monovalent cations which tend to "pull things apart" (interfere with floc formation) and multi-valent cations which "bring things together" (conductive to floc formation.) (Sivasubramanian et al. 2021) Examples of monovalent cations include sodium and potassium.

It is suspected that bacteria release potassium upon exposure to stress thus increasing potassium concentrations, (Increasing the monovalent: multi-valent ratio) which may contribute to dispersed growth.

Examples of multi-valent cations include:

- Calcium
- Magnesium
- Aluminum
- Iron

MULTI-VALENT CATIONS ARE COMMONLY FOUND IN COAGULANT CHEMICALS.

2.6B Causes for Dispersed Filamentous Bacteria Growth

If a filament type is growing dispersed in solution between the flocs the general assumption is that the growth rate of this filament is high enough that the filament no longer needs the floc to compete and is growing rapidly.

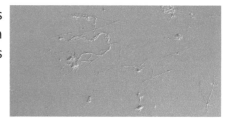

Figure 2.14 dispersed filaments cropped 200x DIC

Additional signs that filamentous bacteria are growing rapidly:

Intracellular PHB (Polyhydroxy Butyrate) Granules

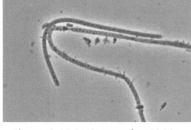

Figure 2.15 PHB granules 1000x phase contrast

PHB are typically, black or blue "dots" within the filaments that serve as "fat storage."

The filament oxidizes as much organic material as it can and stores food later as PHB granules to metabolize further downstream along the process.

ALL FILAMENTS CAN STORE PHB. PHB STORAGE IS MOST COMMON IN FAST GROWING FILAMENTS.

Gonidia

The tip of a filament contains (usually between 3-5) sausage shaped cells.

A Gonidia is sometimes observed in filament types such as Thiothrix and type 021N (Jenkins et al., 2004).

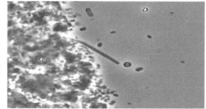

Figure 2.16 gonidia phase cropped 1000x

Rosette Formations

Rosette formations are recognized by filaments radiating from a common area.

Rosettes sometimes occur in Thiothrix and type 021N filaments.

Filament type 0914 often forms structures like Rosettes around inert material.

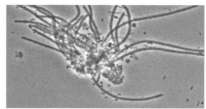

Figure 2.17 Thiothrix rosette 1000x phase cropped

2.6C Causes for Dispersed "Fines"/Dead Cellular Material

- Endogenous (starvation) conditions occur within the system.
- Lack of carbonaceous material.
- Plant is oversized.
- Aerobic digestion/ solids from decanting.

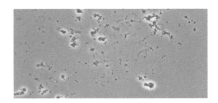
Figure 2.18 dispersed fines_dead cellular 1000x phase

NOTE THAT MANY EXTENDED AERATION SYSTEMS ARE DESIGNED TO OPERATE WITH A FAIR AMOUNT OF ENDOGENY (AEROBIC DIGESTION) OCCURRING HOWEVER IF THIS BECOMES EXCESSIVE, DISPERSED DEAD CELLULAR MATERIAL MAY PROLIFERATE IN THE BULK LIQUID BETWEEN THE FLOCS WHICH CAN ALSO ATTRIBUTE TO PIN FLOC AND "DEAD BUG FOAMS".

- Seasonal/tourism variations in organic loading rates.
- Significance reduction of production from industrial wastewater sources.
- Toxicity- Bacterial death due to disruptions of enzyme functionality.

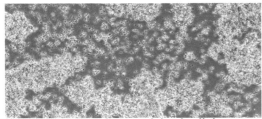
Figure 2.19 dispersed dead cellular material 100x phase contrast

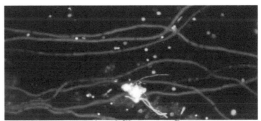
Figure 2.20 dead filaments fluorescent 1000x

- The dead cellular material associated with these events can be responsible for dispersed growth.
- Recycling of dead cellular material through processes such as:
  - o Carryover of anaerobic solids from upstream anaerobic processes.
  - o Poor capture of anaerobic solids in digester centrate return.
  - o Recycling of digested solids from decant of aerobic digesters.

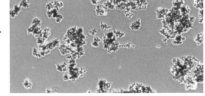
Figure 2.21 anaerobic flocs 100x

2.7 Low Nutrient Availability Defined

For biological treatment to occur in which bacteria produce new cellular material, adequate nutrients must be available for the bacteria at the time the substrate is metabolized. Should nutrients (macro or micronutrients) be limited to the process, cellular growth is shunted to exocellular polysaccharide (slime) growth. Excess polysaccharide formation may pose issues with settling, foaming, and increased viscosity of the mixed liquor. Anthrone testing results of >25% polysaccharide per dry weight of the MLSS suggest the potential of limited nutrient availability occurring within the system. In the Anthrone test procedure, the dry weight of the solids is measured, and the sample is boiled in sulfuric acid, in which a colorimetric method is used to determine the carbohydrate concentration. The carbohydrate concentration is then divided by the dry weight of the biomass as a percentage of polysaccharide.

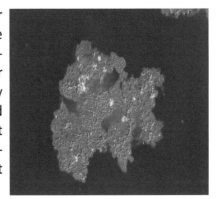
Figure 2.22 elevated polysaccharide low nutrients 200x DIC

23

Note that in practical applications, nutrient deficiency is often periodic and not always a constant. For example, if the BOD loading suddenly increases by 2-3x in concentration, nutrients need to be adjusted accordingly to maintain the desired BOD:N:P ratio. Should adequate nutrients not be available at the time of treatment, polysaccharide build up will occur until the conditions return to where new bug "bodies" may be generated.

2.7A Macronutrients

Nitrogen and Phosphorous are considered the main macronutrients. It is extremely rare for nutrients to be limited in domestic wastewater processes, but in many industrial wastewater systems, nutrient supplementation is needed. Testing the filtered mixed liquor prior to the final liquid solids separation process (i.e. final clarifier) and ensuring adequate N and P residuals are left over is common practice to ensure adequate macronutrients are present.

> *Phosphorous* - It is recommended to always ensure at least 1 mg/L of orthophosphate in the filtered mixed liquor.

> *Nitrogen-* to ensure adequate nitrogen total inorganic nitrogen (TIN= Ammonia + Nitrate + Nitrite) is measured a residual of >1 mg/L TIN is always recommended.

NOTE THAT IT IS RECOMMENDED TO SAMPLE THE FILTERED MIXED LIQUOR (AND NOT THE CLARIFIER EFFLUENT) FOR NUTRIENT RESIDUALS AS NUTRIENTS MAY BE RE-RELEASED IF SEPTIC CONDITIONS OCCUR WITHIN THE CLARIFIER.

2.7B Micronutrients

Micronutrients consist of metals and salts which are typically present in adequate levels of source water. In our experience, micronutrient limitation appears rare however it is possible, especially in instances where distilled water may be used in industrial production processes. Micronutrients include Potassium, Calcium, Magnesium, Sulfur, Sodium, Chloride, Iron, Zinc, Manganese, Copper, Molybdenum, and Cobalt (Jenkins et al., 2004).

Testing for adequate micronutrients is more complex and requires monitoring each micronutrient concentration of g/kg VSS in relationship to Nitrogen present. Micronutrient deficiency may be addressed by adding any necessary micronutrients that are lacking.

2.8 Foaming/Scum in Wastewater Treatment Processes

Several types of foams/scums are commonly encountered in biological wastewater treatment processes with varying consequences from simply aesthetic issues to issues as severe as foam "billowing" over the aeration basin walls or a significant portion of viable biomass needed for treatment becoming entrapped within the foam, compromising treatment performance.

The actual mechanics of foaming are relatively complex, however the important things to note are that gas/air, and a liquid or a solid are needed to stabilize the foam (Jenkins et al., 2004). Solids that are hydrophobic (not water soluble/want to float) in nature also assist in lowering the surface tension and contributing to foaming events. If surfactants are present these may further stabilize and enhance the amount of foam produced.

2.9 Microscopy Considerations for Diagnosing Foam Causes

From practical experience, to accurately diagnose a foam, microscopic eva-luation is needed. It is poor practice, and often leads to incorrect findings to attempt to diagnose a foam without microscopy to confirm any assumptions. It is important to emphasize that due to the higher solids concentrations in most foams/scums it is recommended to dilute the sample to resemble the MLSS concentration below to allow judgement of the floc characteristics.

Figure 2.23 foam on aeration basin

To accurately diagnose a foam sample, the foam must be compared to the underlying mixed liquor/ biomass.

WHILE THE TYPES OF FOAM DESCRIBED IN THE SECTIONS BELOW ARE STRAIGHTFORWARD IN DIAGNOSIS, IT IS ALSO IMPORTANT TO NOTE THAT IT IS FAIRLY COMMON FOR A FOAM TO HAVE MULTIPLE POTENTIAL FACTORS/INFLUENCES. IN PRACTICE, ONE OR MORE CAUSES OF FOAMING MAY OFTEN APPLY.

2.9A Types of Foaming and Techniques for Diagnosis

Actinomycetes-Mycolata Foam (previously recognized as Nocardia or Nocardioform foams)

Actinomycetes-Mycolata foams almost always stain Gram positive when they are alive/viable. Actinomycetes-Mycolata filament types are recog-nized by the true branching characteristics of the filaments. They may contribute to foaming even if they are dead as the mycolic acid within the cell walls of the filaments persists even in death. Mycolic acid within the cell walls of these filament types is hydrophobic and a recognized cause of foaming events (Jenkins et al., 2004).

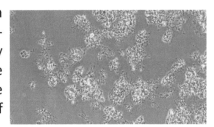

Figure 2.24 Foam Actinomycetes-Mycolata 100x phase

Diagnosing Actinomycetes-Mycolata Foams

Diagnosis of Actinomycetes-Mycolata foams is relatively straightforward in that the relative abundance of Actinomycetes-Mycolata filaments within the foam is compared to the underlying mixed liquor/biomass. If there are significantly higher amounts of Actinomycetes- Mycolata filaments within the foam, then the filaments are diagnosed as the cause or a contributing factor.

Based on our current research, it is suspected that the genetic diversity among Actinomycetes-Mycolata filament types is extremely high (generally unclassified 16SrRNA sequencing reads from the Acidobacteriota and Actinobacteriota phylum).

In municipal systems fats, oils, and grease are the general suspected cause of Actinomycetes-Mycolata. However, it appears Actinomycetes-Mycolata filament types may also compete on other long chain fatty acids or compete well in areas of high COD:BOD ratio and tougher-to-degrade wastes.

Operational Considerations with Actinomycetes-Mycolata Foams

From an operational perspective Actinomycetes-Mycolata foams pose significant concerns when either the-re is potential risk of the foam billowing over the aeration basin or if so many "good bugs" become entrapped within the foam that they are no longer available to treat the incoming wastewater.

NOTE THAT HIGH CONCENTRATIONS OF ACTINOMYCETES-MYCOLATA FILAMENTS WITHIN THE WAS (WASTE ACTIVA-TED SLUDGE) ALSO HAVE THE ABILITY TO CAUSE/CONTRIBUTE TO FOAMING IN DOWNSTREAM PROCESSES SUCH AS ANAEROBIC SLUDGE DIGESTION.

Foam Trapping

When Actinomycetes-Mycolata foams are trapped in a particular area of the plant (i.e. the aeration basin) the filaments gain a competitive advantage and the SRT of these filaments essentially becomes "infinity."

When possible, it is always recommended to physically remove foams or prevent trapping of foams (Khodabakhshi et al., 2015). Configurations such as implementation of overflow rather than underflow as mixed liquor passes through various areas of the treatment plant may also reduce foam trapping (Jenkins et al., 2004). Ideally, foams are removed from the process and mixed directly with sludge (thickened sludge etc.) that is removed (land application etc.). In some instances, success has been reported by transferring foam to an empty tank, chlorinating the foam heavily, and slowly introducing it back into the treatment process.

NOTE THAT IN SOME INSTANCES PHYSICAL REMOVAL OF FOAMS MAY BE DIFFICULT OR IMPOSSIBLE DUE TO THE PLANT DESIGN. ALSO, IF FOAMING IS SEVERE ENOUGH THAT THE FOAM RETURNS WITHIN A DAY OR TWO OF PHYSICAL RE-MOVAL, OTHER CONTROL STRATEGIES MAY PROVE MORE EFFECTIVE.

2.9B Microthrix Filament Foams

Long chain fatty acids, such as oleic acid, formed from septic fats, oils, and grease, are the cause of Microthrix growth (Rossetti et al., 2005). Microth-rix also favors higher SRT values and colder temperatures. The impact and appearance of Microthrix foams is similar to Actinomycetes-Mycolata foams and microscopy is needed to confirm the exact cause.

AS WITH ACTINOMYCETES-MYCOLATA FILAMENT FOAMS, EXCESSIVE MICROTH-RIX IN THE WAS CAN CAUSE FOAMING IN DOWNSTREAM PROCESSES SUCH AS ANAEROBIC DIGESTION.

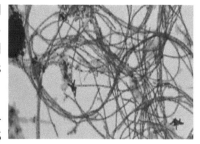

Figure 2.25 Microthrix Neisser 1000x

2.9C Denitrification Foams/Scums

Denitrification foam is formed when nitrogen gas is created through the process of denitrification and the mixing is not satisfactory to drive out nitro-gen gas from the flocs. In order for denitrification to occur the following three variables are needed:

1. Anoxic conditions

2. Presence of nitrate

3. A carbon source

Figure 2.26 denitrification

Most notoriously, denitrification scum/foam is associated with floating sludge in the final clarifiers. Floating sludge issues can be problematic if the sludge rises on the outside of the clarifier baffle and travels into the clarifier effluent leaving as suspended solids. Denitrification foam may also form in areas such as anaerobic zones, anoxic zones, and aeration basins.

NOTE THAT IT IS POSSIBLE FOR DENITRIFICATION TO OCCUR INSIDE OF THE FLOC REGARDLESS OF WHETHER THERE IS A MEASURABLE DO RESIDUAL IN THE AERATION BASIN SHOULD ANOXIC CONDITIONS PERSIST IN THE FLOC INTERIOR.

Diagnosing Denitrification Foam/Scum

It is common to observe significantly larger flocs in a denitrification foam/scum than in the underlying mixed liquor. This phenomenon is related to nitrogen gas entrapment within the flocs. In general, the average floc size in a denitrification foam tends to be at least 1.5x the size of the underlying mixed liquor (M. Richard, Personal Communication).

2.9D "Dead Bug Foams"

When wastewater bacteria die, cell lysis occurs, and the bugs release their cell contents leaving behind dead "bug bodies". These dead "bug bodies" are hydrophobic in nature and a recognized contributor of foaming in wastewater processes.

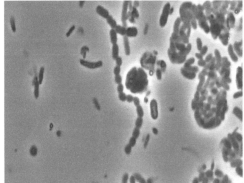

Figure 2.27 dead bug foam fluorescent 1000x

Common Causes for "Dead Bug Foams"

- Sudden "die offs" caused by stress or toxicity experienced within the plant.
- Recycling of "fines" through the process.
- Solids recycled through aerobic digester decant processes.
- Anaerobic solids carried over from upstream anaerobic processes or poor centrate capture.
- Old sludge/death occurs through endogenous processes/ starvation.
- Occasionally dead bug foams may be attributed to the "blooming" and subsequent die off of a particular higher life form organism (i.e. testate amoebae).

2.9E Filament Type 1863 Foam

Figure 2.28 type 1863 1000x phase cropped

Filament type 1863 is recognized to contribute to wastewater foaming events. The recognized root cause of type 1863 filaments are fats, oils, and grease. Filament type 1863 is often correlated with the genus Acinetobacter and is suspected to generally grow in collection systems (Dueholm et al. 2021).

IN OUR EXPERIENCE IT APPEARS MORE RELIABLE TO CORRELATE TYPE 1863 FILAMENTS TO RECENT FATS, OILS, AND GREASE THAN ASSUMING A LOW SRT IS PRESENT, ALTHOUGH THESE FILAMENTS ARE ALSO RECOGNIZED TO COMPETE WELL AT LOW SRT VALUES (I.E. THE COLLECTION SYSTEM).

Diagnosing Type 1863 Foams

As with Actinomycetes-Mycolata and Microthrix foams, diagnosis of filament type 1863 foams is achieved through a significantly higher presence of type 1863 filaments within the foam compared to the underlying mixed liquor.

2.9F Surfactant Foams

There are many potential surfactants that may enter wastewater treatment processes with varying degrees of impact ranging from low/insignificant to toxicity/failure of biological treatment. Surfactants may be anionic, cationic, or nonionic in charge and may have varying degrees of biodegradability ranging from slowly biodegradable to non-biodegradable.

Biodegradable surfactants are generally complex and difficult for bacteria to metabolize.

Figure 2.29 surfactant foam

Biodegradation of surfactant foams is aided by warmer temperatures and higher SRT values.

Diagnosing Surfactant Foams

Surfactant foams are the most likely foam to be successfully diagnosed through visual observation due to their white-frothy soap-like appearance. Surface tension of <60 dynes/cm are recognized to be a cause of surfactant foams (Jenkins et al., 2004).

It is common to observe high amounts of filamentous bacteria or flocs that have high filaments within these foams, however it is likely this occurrence is related to incidental entrapment rather than certain filament types being directly responsible for foaming events. It is good practice to shake a sample prior to microscopic evaluation and determine if a foam develops.

Because surfactants decrease surface tension values, they also have the potential to interfere with dissolved oxygen transfer and in many instances low dissolved oxygen concentrations or additional oxygen demand may be noticed in their presence.

AS A GENERAL PRECAUTION, ANY TIME A SURFACTANT FOAM IS OBSERVED IN ANY AREA OF THE PLANT, IT IS A GOOD IDEA TO PERFORM A THOROUGH MICROSCOPIC EVALUATION WITH EXTRA EMPHASIS ON THE HEALTH OF THE BIOMASS TO DETERMINE IF ANY OPERATIONAL CHANGES SHOULD BE MADE.

2.9G Polysaccharide Foams

Exocellular polysaccharide is hydrophobic in nature and can contribute to foaming. Excess polysaccharide may be produced by the following:

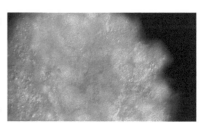

- Low nutrient availability.
- Excess abundance of zoogloea bacteria type microorganisms.
- Other stresses. Anytime bacteria are exposed to stress, polysaccharide is created as a defense mechanism.

Figure 2.30 polysaccharide scum

2.9H Miscellaneous Scums and Foulants

The items below appear as scums or foulants and are occasionally observed in various processes.

Stalked Ciliate Scum

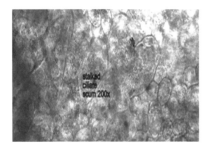

Figure 2.31 stalked ciliate scum 200x

While it is generally accepted that biological wastewater treatment processes perform at their best when stalked ciliates are the predominant higher life form there are some exceptions (notice that this statement is a reoccurring theme in biological wastewater treatment processes).

Stalked ciliate "blooms" may occur if conditions exist in which stalked ciliates can outcompete other higher life form organisms. "Blooming events" often create an excessive number of stalked ciliates which may become viscous and slimy and form a scum. In most of these instances it is believed that high amounts of dispersed single cell bacteria are the root cause for the stalked ciliate "bloom".

Common Areas for Stalked Ciliate Scum

From a competition standpoint, stalked ciliate scums tend to develop in areas where stalked ciliates can attach to something and outcompete other higher life form organisms for dispersed single cell bacteria through their filtering/ "funneling" capabilities. Common areas include:

- UV disinfection areas
- Channels prior to tertiary filtration
- Inline DO probes

NOTE THAT STALKED CILIATE SCUM TYPICALLY APPEARS SLIMY/VISCOUS AND COMMONLY STICKS TO PIPETTE TIPS. MICROSCOPIC ANALYSIS IS NEEDED TO CONFIRM THE EXISTENCE OF THESE SCUMS.

Tubiflex Worm Scum

Tubiflex worms are typically visible to the human eye and appear as red worms that can grow up to as long as 1-2 inches. Overgrowth of Tubiflex worms often causes a scum formation that in severe instances can cause plugging in pumps and other blockages in pipes.

Figure 2.32 tubiflex worms

Areas of Potential Tubiflex Worm Growth

- Any area in which there is septic or "rotting sludge".
- Final clarifiers in which the bottom scraper is not working properly.
- Dead spots in aeration basins where sludge settling accumulates.
- Solid buildup in post EQ basins.

Filamentous "Hardballs"

When certain filament types are growing at excessive abundance, they can become "slimy" and form a hard ball like scum. These scums do not appear to float but can act as foulants in areas such as tertiary filtration and UV disinfection.

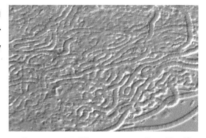

Figure 2.33 filamentous hardball cropped from 1000x DIC

Filamentous Morphotypes in Which "Hardball" Formations Have Been Observed

- Type 021N.
- Thiothrix.
- Sphaerotilus/type 1701.
- Nostocoida limicola types.

Beggiatoa Scum

Beggiatoa filament types are recognized by their motility, wide cell diameter (>2 µm), and they also typically contain intracellular sulfur granules. Beggiatoa filament types generally occur in fixed film processes at a high F/M (food to microorganism) ratio. It is suspected that Beggiatoa growth may also occur in collection systems, however in these instances Beggiatoa filament types do not appear to generally compete well in downstream suspended growth processes.

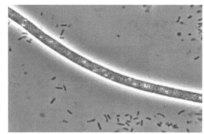

Figure 2.34 Beggiatoa 1000x phase contrast

Common Areas to Suspect Beggiatoa Scum

- White billowy growth in rotating biological contactor (RBC) processes.
- Occasionally in ponds where there is a place for a septic biofilm to form.

BEGGIATOA SCUMS MUST BE DIAGNOSED THROUGH MICROSCOPIC OBSERVATION.

Chapter 3:

Microscopy Fundamentals
Co-Written By Scott Miller of Microscope Central

3.1 Types of Microscopes Recommended

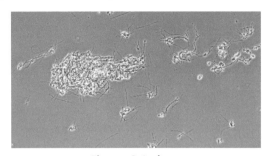

Figure: 3.1 phase

Figure: 3.2 brightfield

3.1A Necessary Criteria

When deciding what microscope to purchase, the following are necessary criteria for conducting evaluations based on the procedures outlined in this textbook:

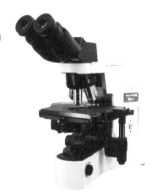

- Phase contrast 10x and 100x oil immersion objectives.
  - o 20x and 40x objectives are useful but not essential.
- A brightfield option for Gram and Neisser Stain.
- Optional:
  - o If camera usage is desired a trinocular head is needed.
  - o If no camera/photography is desired binocular heads are sufficient.

Figure: 3.3 phase contrast micro-scope

3.1B Common Vendors Who Produce Good Microscopes for Wastewater Applications

- Olympus (Premium)
- Leica
- Nikon
- Accu-Scope
- Zeiss
- Labomed

IN THE LONG RUN, IF INVESTING IN A MICROSCOPE IT IS RECOMMENDED TO SPEND A LITTLE EXTRA MONEY AND GET A MICROSCOPE THAT WILL BE FUNCTIONAL FOR MANY YEARS. CHEAPLY-MADE MICROSCOPES OFTEN LOOK GOOD ON THE INITIAL PURCHASE, HOWEVER OVER TIME PROBLEMS OFTEN OCCUR WITH THE PHASE RINGS (ESSENTIAL), THE ADJUSTMENT MECHANISMS, AND THE LIGHTING. IN SUMMARY, YOU GET WHAT YOU PAY FOR. IN ADDITION, THERE ARE MANY "BRANDS" OUT THERE THAT HAVE LITTLE TO NO SUPPORT AND DO NOT SELL REPLACEMENT / REPAIR PARTS.

3.2 How Phase Contrast Microscopy Works

Not all phase contrast microscopes are created equally. The simple explanation is that each objective has a different size ring inside of it. Each objective is typically labeled with Ph1, Ph2, or Ph3. The 10x and 20x objective are Ph1, the 40x will be Ph2, and the 100x will be Ph3. The ring inside the objective must match the ring called the phase annulus which is inserted into the condenser. Once the microscope is properly aligned, and the two rings are superimposed you are "in phase." There are three different ways to insert the phase annulus into the condenser.

1. **Individual snap on pieces-** This method is an economical method and is not recommended as you physically have to add / remove components from the bottom of your condenser as you change objectives. It can slow you down, lead to misalignment of the phase rings, and / or breaking and losing the parts.

2. **A phase slider-** This method involves inserting a bar into the slot of your condenser. You slide the bar left / right to put the corresponding phase annulus in position to match the objective. The issue with this method is that some models do not have enough space to have all phase annuli on the same bar, so you will need to remove one slider and insert another. The second part is that the slider's position is not visible as it is hidden under the stage, so you need to look under the stage to verify which position you are in.

3. **A phase turret-** This is the most expensive method, but also the most convenient. This method involves a wheel that contains the phase annuli all in one. You simply rotate the wheel as you change objectives. The position of the phase turret is clear and right in front of you. A phase turret will typically have a darkfield spot on it in addition to phase and brightfield.

IN SUMMARY THERE ARE VARIOUS WAYS TO ACHIEVE PHASE CONTRAST WITH DIFFERING QUALITY LEVELS.

3.3 Alignment of the Phase Rings

To be "in phase" you must superimpose the phase ring in the objective on the corresponding phase annulus inserted into the condenser. The first step is to align your microscope for Kohler illumination (if applicable). Once this is done you can begin to align the phase rings. This process is made easier by a phase centering telescope. You remove an eyepiece and insert the phase centering telescope which allows you to focus on the two rings. The phase ring in the objective does not move, you will move the phase annulus in the condenser. The individual snap-on pieces typically have two thumbscrews, the phase slider is sometimes pre-aligned, and you cannot move the annulus, in which case you move them with Allen wrenches. The phase turret condenser most of the time will have Allen wrenches that are already built into the condenser, and you simply push in and turn them. The other method is that the condenser has two dials underneath that you can rotate to move the annulus. Once you complete the phase alignment, the position should hold unless someone disrupts the microscope (How to Center for Phase Contrast (n.d.), How To Center For Koehler Illumination, (n.d.)).

3.4 Microscope Supplies and Vendors

Microscope Slides
- 25x 75 mm (frosted edges optional)

Microscope Cover Slips
- 22X22 mm No 1

Sample Vendors for Slides and Cover Slips
- Carolina
- Sigma Aldrich
- NC Labs
- Thermo Fisher
- Cardinal Health

Gram Stain Kit
- #1 Crystal Violent
- #2 Iodine
- #3 Decolorizer
- #4 Safarin

Sample Vendors for Gram Stain Kits
- Thermo Fisher
- NC Labs
- Weber Scientific
- Thomas Scientific

Neisser Stain Kit
- #1 Methylene Blue Crystal Violent Solution
- #2 Bismark Brown

Sample Vendors for Neisser Stain Kits
- NC Labs
- Sigma Aldrich
- Atom Scientific

Reverse India Ink Stain
- India ink

Sample Vendors for India Ink
- Higgins Waterproof Black India Ink
- Speedball 2-Ounce Super Black
- Black Velvet Waterproof India Ink

3.5 Reference for Microscope Settings Based on Desired Application

3.5A Low Power Microscopic Evaluation
- 10x phase contrast objective
- Phase 1 ring
- Slide and cover slip (no oil)

Figure: 3.4 microscope lens

3.5B High Power Microscopic Evaluation
- 100x oil immersion phase contrast objective
- Phase 3 ring (or sometimes phase 4 or labeled slightly different depending on scope)
- Slide and cover slip
- Oil drop (type A oil recommended) over cover slip

Figure: 3.5 microscope lens

3.5C Reverse India Ink Stain

- 10x phase contrast objective or higher
- Slide and cover slip
- India ink

3.5D Gram and Neisser Stain

- 100x oil immersion objective
- Slide (no coverslip)
- Drop of oil over prepared slide prior to observation
- Brightfield magnification (no phase)

Figure: 3.7 Gram and Neisser staining

3.6 Troubleshooting Common Microscope Problems

1. My specimen will not come into focus:
   - Verify that the slide is on correctly with the coverslip on.
   - If the stage will not come up high enough check the stage focus lock which is typically found on the left side of the microscope inwards of the coarse focus.
   - If your eyepieces are not focusing make sure that they are both set to the zero mark, or relatively close.

2. The camera is not parfocal with the eyepieces:
   - Some camera adapters have focusing capabilities, adjust the focus on your c-mount to match the focus on the eyepieces.
   - Check the eyepieces and make sure they are close to the zero mark, if they are both focused all the way up, or down it will not be parfocal with the camera.
   - More can be found at: https://microscopecentral.com/pages/troubleshooting-common-microscope-issues

3.7 Microscope Cameras

There is a misconception that higher megapixel (MP) means better. This is not the case for microscope cameras. The ideal range is 3-5 MP, and you should not buy a camera justifying the purchase due to the higher megapixel. There are other factors that are more important such as the sensor and the physical size of the pixels. The larger the pixel size, the greater the light gathering capabilities of the camera. This will result in higher frames per second (FPS), and higher resolution images. Since phase contrast is a lower-light application, a camera with large pixel size is more desirable (Microscope Cameras & Mega Pixels, n.d; Choosing A Microscope Camera, n.d.).

Figure: 3.8 camera

There are cameras on the market that offer USB output, USB & HDMI output, or USB, HDMI, and Wi-Fi output. You can even get cameras that have viewing screens attached to them for an all-in-one streamlined solution. We do not recommend the tablet cameras as you need to touch the camera to control the camera / capture images, and this can disrupt your sample resulting in poor images (Choosing A Microscope Camera, n.d.). We suggest cameras with screens that have a mouse that you plug into them to control the camera such as:

- The View4K 4K Digital Microscope Camera with Screen (with HDMI, USB, and Wifi).
- The Accu-Scope Excelis HD Lite Microscope Camera w/ 11.6" Screen.

Both microscope cameras and more information on general camera parameters can be found at microscopecentral.com.

3.8 Optional Additions

For wastewater applications, phase contrast microscopy is sufficient. There are certain applications that call for DIC or Fluorescence.

3.8A DIC

DIC is also known as Nomarski and is a contrast technique that offers higher resolution, more contrast, and more depth to your specimens than phase contrast. Overall, the image will be higher resolution and offer a more three-dimensional appearance. DIC involves more moving parts and is more complex in operation than a phase contrast microscope. You will need special objectives, prisms, and other components and a DIC microscope can be around $30,000. In practical experience DIC is useful for identification of morphotype and abundance ranking at high power magnification due to its 3-dimensional aspects.

Figure: 3.9 DIC

3.8B Fluorescence

A fluorescence microscope has an illuminator that has light that passes through the objective lenses. A fluorescence microscope has a turret which allows you to engage different filters. These filters are paired to the probe or reagents you use and when engaged, the sample will illuminate and show the cells that react with the probe and filter selected. A fluorescence microscope can range in price from $5,000 - $20,000. Fluorescence microscopes are used for FISH (Fluorescence In Situ Hybridization).

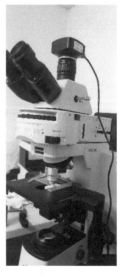

Figure: 3.10 fluorescent microscope

Chapter 4:

Low Power Microscopy Observation Criteria

Background

It may be beneficial to consider wastewater microscopy evaluations as two separate tests. Low-power-only observations and a full microscopic evaluation (low-power and high-power observations, filament type identification etc.) The frequency of the more detailed/inclusive microscopic evaluation is determined by how often the influent loading characteristics change. The frequency of these "full microscopy evaluations" may range from periods of every few days to every few sludge cycles depending on the circumstances. The "shortened" low-power observation can typically be completed within 5-10 minutes with proper training and may be done every day as part of normal in-house testing.

Practical Application

When low-power observation is used, the general goal is to get an overall "big picture" view of the sludge characteristics. When we provide training, we focus on low-power observation microscopy with an emphasis on "calibrating" the operations team so that there is consistency in these daily observations regardless of who is performing the microscopy. Should there be a notable change such as an increase in dispersed growth, an increase of filamentous bacteria, an increase of filamentous bacteria impact on the overall floc structure, a notable change in the floc structure, or a significant change of higher life form organisms etc., a more complete evaluation is then warranted. For the thorough observations, it is recommended to have a small number of people assigned to this task and it is often useful to use periodic split sampling with a trusted professional to validate and calibrate the findings. The most important aspect of low-power magnification is the ability to use it as a "red flag" that something has changed, and that further observation or action may be warranted.

Details and Documentation

The in-house reporting goals of low-power microscopic evaluations may vary somewhat depending on individual circumstances; however, we recommend prioritizing efficiency. Personally, we do not see value in techniques such as counting higher life form organisms and detailed daily reports of low-power microscopy observations. Recommendations for documentation include filling out a standard bench sheet or simply writing in the daily logbook any notable changes from what would be considered "baseline" conditions. If daily low-power microscopy is longer than 15 minutes per day, it is likely that efficiency in the process may be lacking.

4.1 Slide Preparation

The technique used for preparing a slide for low-power magnification (10 or 20x objective lens, 100x or 200x magnification) is referred to as the "soft smash" and consists of placing approximately 20 µL of sample on a slide and adding a cover slip. Once the cover slip is placed over the sample, using a paper towel the index finger is used to gently press the slide.

4.1A Slide Preparation Considerations

- We recommend using 22x22 mm #1 cover slips (you can fit two cover slips on a slide).
- For slides, our preference is 1mm-1.2mm thickness and a 1" by 3" slide size.
- It is essential that the sample is representative of the mixed liquor and should be properly mixed prior to pipetting.
- Press gently on the cover slip and not too hard, or there is risk of crushing the higher life form organisms.
- Never touch the center of the slides or the cover slips; always use the edges.
- Be careful, as it is often easy for cover slips to stick together (make sure there is only 1).

- Personally, I am not a big fan of re-using slides and cover slips since if these are not cleaned properly there is potential to alter the observations.
- For samples that possess suspended solids concentrations of 1%, (10,000 mg/L) dilution may be required to properly determine floc size and other important characteristics.
  o Should the sample be diluted for low-power observation this should be noted.
    - If possible, always try to judge dispersed growth without dilution or in worst case scenarios for samples with foam/scum, keep in mind the dilution factor when looking at dispersed growth abundance.

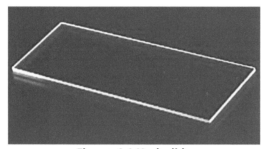

Figure: 4.1 Hach slide

Figure: 4.2 Hach cover slip

4.2 Judging Floc Morphology

In practical experience a minimum of 20-30 flocs should be viewed before making any general observations about the floc characteristics. The following items may apply to one or more:

☐ Firm   ☐ Irregular Shape ☐ Open/Diffuse   ☐ Weak   ☐ Viscous   ☐ Pin Flocs Predominant

4.2A Floc Morphology Characteristics

Firm

Flocs are densely compacted with low amounts of void space. Firm flocs generally are expected to settle well.

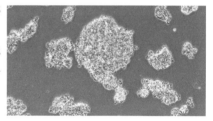

Figure: 4.3 firm floc low filament abundance 100x phase

- In bulking events in which firm flocs are observed, filamentous bacteria are usually extending from the flocs or bridging flocs together.
- Filamentous bacteria abundance can vary widely and if filaments are present within the floc and not impacting the floc strength, settling problems generally do not occur.

Irregular Shape

Usually, flocs with a higher filament abundance tend to become irregular in shape, in which the filaments dictate the size of the flocs.

- Strong or weak flocs can both exist with irregular shapes.

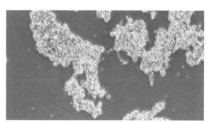

Figure: 4.4 irregular shape flocs

Open/Diffuse

Typically, flocs that are open/diffuse in structure contain large "void" spaces created by filamentous bacteria growing within the flocs.

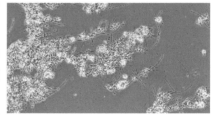

Figure: 4.5 diffuse floc 100x phase

- Filamentous bulking associated with open/diffuse floc structure occurs when the overall density of the floc is weakened, creating buoyancy in the settling characteristics.
    - o Remedial action with selective chlorination may often prove difficult with open/diffuse flocs as "collateral damage" may occur in the process.
        - Depending on the situation, there are some instances when settling aids/ coagulants may be a better choice if needed.

Weak

Often, but not always, there may be overlap with weak flocs and flocs classified as "open/diffuse". Weak flocs lack dense characteristics and may appear "fluffy".

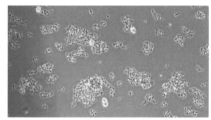

Figure: 4.6 weak flocs 100x

Viscous

Viscous flocs contain high amounts of exocellular polysaccharide.

- Elevated polysaccharide may be diagnosed through the reverse India ink stain staining.

- Viscous flocs may either settle slowly due to "true slime bulking" (in which the exocellular polysaccharide layers interfere with the compaction ability of the sludge) or may settle slowly due to weakened floc structure and the hydrophobic nature of the polysaccharide.

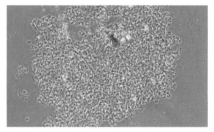

Figure: 4.7 viscous flocs 100x phase

Pin Floc

Pin floc are <50 μm in dimension and may occur when there are excessive SRT values, excessive endogeny (low F/M), or in instances of chronic stress (or a combination of the above).

- Pin flocs may either settle quickly, often leaving behind a turbid supernatant or can also settle slowly due to "pin ball" actions of charge repellent countering the gravitational impact of the flocs.

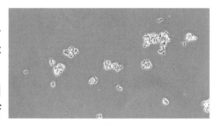

Figure: 4.8 pin floc 100x phase

4.3 Dispersed Growth Characteristics

Dispersed growth may be recognized as growth occurring in the bulk liquid between flocculated bacteria. Dispersed growth may consist of dispersed single cell bacteria, dispersed filamentous bacteria, dispersed tetrads, dispersed "fines"/dead cellular material or any combination of the above (Jenkins et al., 2004) Dispersed growth may be ranked as:

☐ Few   ☐ Some ☐ Common ☐ Very Common   ☐ Abundant   ☐ Excessive

4.4 Higher Life Form Organisms

Background

In general, higher life form organisms are believed to make up 5-20% by weight of the MLSS concentration (Jenkins et al., 2004). Bacteria (not higher life form organisms) are responsible for the majority of BOD removal and the higher life form organisms generally act as "polishers" of dispersed single cell bacteria. Relatively speaking, as prey densities of dispersed single cell bacteria decrease, higher life form organisms become more sophisticated at capturing substrate. Note that it is possible for good wastewater treatment to occur in plants with and without the presence of higher life form organisms.

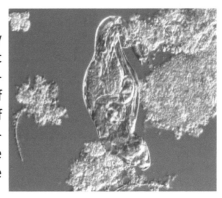

Figure: 4.9 rotifer cropped from 200x DIC

4.4A Practical Application of Higher Life Form Organism Observations

From a microscopy standpoint, it is good practice to note which higher life form organisms are observed in a sample as well as which (if any) higher life form organism is predominant. It is also important to keep in mind that the mixture of higher life form organisms may change rapidly depending on conditions and it is therefore not considered good operational practice to attempt to link sludge age or process control changes (such as changes to wasting rates) to higher life form organisms (Jenkins et al., 2004).

SIMPLY PUT, HIGHER LIFE FORM ORGANISMS ARE A "PIECE OF THE PUZZLE," HOWEVER MORE INFORMATION IS NEEDED TO DEVELOP "BIG PICTURE" CONDITIONS BASED ON MICROSCOPY OBSERVATIONS.

SEE THE CHAPTER ON HIGHER LIFE FORM ORGANISMS LATER IN THIS TEXT FOR MORE IN-DEPTH COVERAGE.

4.5 Ranking Filamentous Bacteria Abundance at 10x and 20x

Background

It is important to note that in many instances, filaments may be located within the flocs and often may be overlooked at lower power magnification. Therefore, only a preliminary ranking for filamentous abundance is obtained from low power magnifications. This ranking may change if higher power microscopy is included and ultimately the filamentous bacteria impact on the floc structure takes priority.

Practical Application

From practical experience, it is useful to work within the scaling systems, but also keep some flexibility and ability to add notes and explanations that may help to describe what is viewed. In many instances a combined score (such as 3.5- common to very common) may present a more detailed picture. In summary, do not become fixated on the guidelines, but rather focus on communicating findings effectively and leaving room for flexibility.

4.5A Scale for Ranking Filamentous Bacteria Abundance (0-6)

Value	Abundance	Description	
0	None	No filaments observed.	
1	Few	Low/insignificant filaments observed.	
2	Some	Per average floc viewed <5 filaments are observed.	(Jenkins et al., 2004)
3	Common	Per average floc viewed 5 filaments are observed.	
4	Very Common	Per average floc viewed 5-20 filaments are observed.	
5	Abundant	Per average floc viewed >20 filaments are observed.	
6	Excessive	There appears to be a higher % of filaments than flocculated bacteria.	

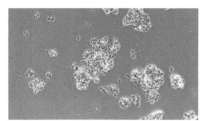

Figure: 4.10 low filaments 100x

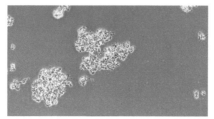

Figure: 4.11 common filaments 100x

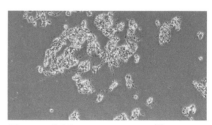

Figure: 4.12 very common filaments 100x

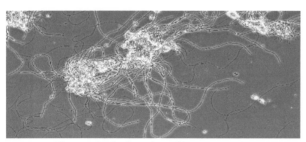

Figure: 4.13 abundant filaments 100x

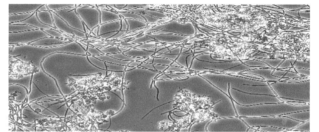

Figure: 4.14 excessive filaments 100x

Notes for Interpreting Filament Abundance

- Filamentous bacteria must be ranked "common" or greater to be judged as significant in terms of applying any associated causes.
- Often, once filamentous bacteria reach very common or greater abundance, there is a corresponding increase in the SVI values of the sludge.

4.6 Location of Filamentous Bacteria

☐ Within the flocs   ☐ Dispersed in solution   ☐ Extending from the flocs

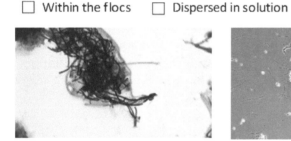

Figure: 4.15 filaments in floc 1000x Neisser

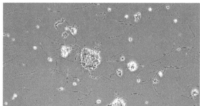

Figure: 4.16 dispersed filaments 100x

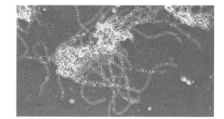

Figure: 4.17 abundant filaments 100x

NOTE THAT ONE OR MORE OF THE ABOVE MAY BE CHECKED. IF MULTIPLE DESCRIPTIONS APPLY, IT IS GOOD PRACTICE TO MAKE A NOTE OF WHICH SCENARIO IS PREDOMINANT OR NOTE THE ESTIMATED % OF EACH.

4.7 Judging Filamentous Bacteria's Impact on Overall Floc Structure

Background

Simply stated, the stronger and denser the floc structure, the more filaments may typically be supported without a corresponding increase in SVI values. In terms of floc structure quality, the impact of filamentous bacteria on the overall floc structure may often be considered more significant than the actual filamentous bacteria abundance.

☐ Low/Insignificant   ☐ Moderate   ☐ High

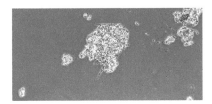
Figure: 4.18 low impact on floc

Figure: 4.19 moderate impact on floc

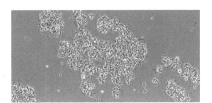
Figure: 4.20 high impact on floc

4.7A Practical Applications

- Filamentous bacteria themselves are not problematic (they are good BOD degraders) and it is generally considered beneficial for the overall floc structure if filamentous bacteria are ranked common in abundance (providing a "backbone" structure for flocculated bacteria).

  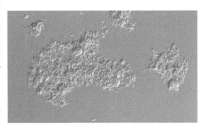
  Figure: 4.21 strong flocs with high filament abundance 200x DIC

  o Despite the above statement, note that strong flocs may exist with or without the presence of filamentous bacteria (Jenkins et al., 2004).

- In many instances strong flocs may exist, supporting "very common" or greater filamentous bacteria abundance without causing problems. Whereas if floc structure is weak, SVI values may be impacted at as low as "common-very common" filament abundance.

FOR EACH PLANT THERE MAY BE VARYING DEGREES TO WHICH "CONDITIONS" BECOME "PROBLEMS" AND THUS VARYING DEGREES TO WHICH OPERATIONAL INTERVENTION IS SUGGESTED.

4.8 Ranking of Traditional Zoogloea Bacteria Morphotypes

Background

Zoogloea bacteria morphotypes are recognized by the thick polysaccharide layer surrounding each individual cell. Zoogloea bacteria types commonly exist as either "globular zoogloea" or "fingered zoogloea" and are most commonly associated with either the Thauera and Zoogloea genus (note that other genera and species may also possess the "zoogloea" morphotype including suspected unclassified tax ID numbers at the time of this writing)(Táncsics et al., 2019).

At moderate abundance, zoogloea bacteria types are considered beneficial for floc formation (the polysaccharide acts as "glue") however if zoogloea bacteria abundance is too high problems may occur, as discussed in Chapter 2.

☐ Few   ☐ Some ☐ Common ☐ Very Common   ☐ Abundant   ☐ Excessive

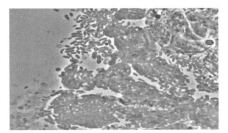
Figure: 4.22 fingered zoogloea cropped from 1000x phase

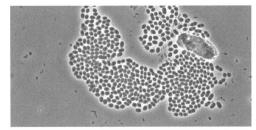
Figure: 4.23 globular zoogloea cropped from 1000x DIC

Scoring System for Zoogloea Bacteria Morphotypes

While the same numerical ranking system exists for zoogloea bacteria types as filamentous bacteria, the actual methodology for scoring is somewhat more subjective. However, it may be "calibrated" with experience.

4.9 Reverse India Ink Stain

Background

Judging the reverse India ink stain is often the most challenging aspect in wastewater microscopic evaluation. Rather than the color produced, judgement of "normal vs. elevated" is related to the amount of space that is impenetrable to the India ink particles in the procedure. Note that it is common for polysaccharide to differentiate between flocs observed and the findings need to be clearly communicated.

☐ Normal   ☐ Elevated   ☐ Mix of Normal and Elevated

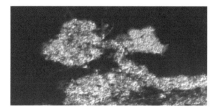 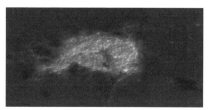 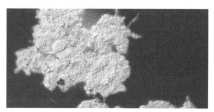

Figure: 4.24 normal (left) elevated (right) polysaccharide

Figure: 4.25 normal polysaccharide 400x DIC

Figure: 4.26 elevated polysaccharide zoogloea 400x DIC

Practical Application

We suggest selecting which of the above options in the boxes is predominant and if there is variance observed, note the estimated percentage of elevated versus normal polysaccharide. It is good practice to view a minimum of 20-30 flocs to determine a polysaccharide judgement.

4.9A Reverse India Ink Procedure

- Mix the India ink thoroughly (ensure the cap is secured tightly before shaking to mix).
  - o Always ensure that India ink container is sealed when unused as prolonged exposure to air deteriorates the India ink quality.
- Place a slide on a section of paper towel.
- Place one drop of India ink on the slide.
- Place one drop of evenly mixed liquor over the India ink.
- Using the side/edge of a cover slip mix the India ink and mixed liquor.
- Place a cover slip over the combination of India ink and mixed liquor.
- Using the paper towel or a piece of absorbent paper, press the cover slip gently.
  - o Any excess ink or activated sludge may be discarded.

Notes for Practical Application

- The slide must be pressed adequately to retain enough India ink and sample to be viewed under the microscope.
  - o Over-pressing may dispel too much India ink and under-pressing has potential to cause difficulty in evaluating polysaccharide in individual flocs.
  - o The amount to press is a learned through trial and error may also vary depending upon each individual sample analyzed.
    - Some people prefer a "gradient press" in which force is applied to different areas of the cover slip (the author prefers the trial-and-error method).

- Phase contrast 10x, 20x, and 40x are the most effective resolutions for observation.

OFTEN TIMES, TURNING DOWN THE LIGHTING ON THE MICROSCOPE MAY AID IN INTERPRETING RESULTS.

4.10 Example of a Low Power Magnification Bench Sheet

Low Power Microscopic Evaluation Bench Sheet

Sample ID

Sample Collection Date

Sample Evaluation Date

Lab Tech Name

1) Floc morphology (per average floc viewed)
☐ Firm ☐ Irregular Shape ☐ Open/Diffuse ☐ Weak ☐ Viscous ☐ Pin Flocs Predominant

2) Dispersed growth in the bulk liquid between the flocs was ranked:
☐ Few ☐ Some ☐ Common ☐ Very Common ☐ Abundant ☐ Excessive

3) Higher life form organisms viewed included: ☐ Flagellates ☐ Naked Amoebae ☐ Testate Amoebae ☐ Rotifer
☐ Free Swimming Ciliates ☐ Stalked Ciliates ☐ Bristle Worm ☐ Nematode ☐ Water Bear (Tardigrade)
☐ Gastrotrich ☐ Crustacean ☐ Daphnia ☐ Green Algae ☐ Diatoms ☐ N/A

4) The predominant higher life form organism viewed was:
☐

5) Filamentous bacteria were ranked:
☐ Few ☐ Some ☐ Common ☐ Very Common ☐ Abundant ☐ Excessive

6) Filamentous bacteria were located predominantly:
☐ Within the flocs ☐ Dispersed in solution ☐ Extending from the flocs

7) Filamentous bacteria impact on the overall floc structure was judged as:
☐ Low/Insignificant ☐ Moderate ☐ High

8) Traditional zoogloeal bacteria morphotypes were ranked:
☐ Few ☐ Some ☐ Common ☐ Very Common ☐ Abundant ☐ Excessive

9) Reverse India ink stain interpretation of polysaccharide per average floc was judged as:
☐ Normal ☐ Elevated ☐ Mix of Normal and Elevated

Chapter 5:

Higher Life Form Organisms

Background

In general, the higher life form organisms are believed to make up 5-20% by weight of the MLSS concentration. Bacteria (not higher life form organisms) are responsible for most BOD removal and the higher life form organisms generally act as "polishers" of dispersed single cell bacteria. Relatively speaking, as prey densities of dispersed single cell bacteria decrease, higher life form organisms become more sophisticated at capturing substrate (Jenkins et al., 2004). Note that it is possible for good wastewater treatment to occur in plants with or without the presence of higher life form organisms.

Types of Higher Life Form Organisms

Note: Some Sections Contain Excerpts from Treatment Plant Operator's "Bug of the Month" and may also be viewed at https://www.tpomag.com/tags/bug-of-the-month

5.1 Flagellates

Flagellates are small (5 to 20 μm) and move using one or more long, whip-like flagella. Flagellates consist of over 8,500 species (Wikipedia, 2021a). Many flagellate species found in activated sludge feed on soluble organic matter and oftentimes correlate with higher soluble biochemical oxygen demand (BOD) levels. Some flagellates function colonially while others exist as a single cell. Flagellates multiply through binary fission with some species containing cyst stages. In general, flagellates prefer soluble nutrients or dead or decaying organic matter. Flagellates can compete with bacteria but can't keep up with their logarithmic growth rate, so they only predominate when organic material is high (i.e., "young sludge" conditions). Flagellates also often are the first protozoa to emerge after a toxic or stressful event. Seeing low amounts of flagellates is typical in well operating systems. When flagellates are present at high abundance further investigation is often warranted.

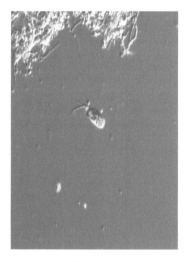

Figure 5.1 flagellate 200x DIC cropped

5.2 Naked Amoebae

Naked amoebae are unicellular organisms lacking cell walls that can alter their shape as well as eat through movement of their pseudopodia ("false feet") (Protozoa: The Naked Amoeba, n.d.). Amoebae do not form a specific taxonomic group; however, they are found in every lineage of Eukaryotes. Most commonly, proliferation of naked amoebae in wastewater treatment processes is associated with plant start-up conditions and/or conditions in which there is high levels of remaining soluble carbonaceous material available.

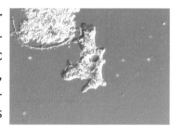

Figure 5.1 flagellate 200x DIC cropped

5.3 Testate Amoebae

Testate amoebae occur commonly in many types of wastewater treatment plants. They differentiate from naked amoebae in that they have a "test" (shell), which offers protection against many environmental stresses, such as harsh conditions, low dissolved oxygen concentrations, and more. Testate amoebae have not been successfully correlated to any specific sludge age or F/M conditions (Jenkins et al., 2004). High genetic diversity exists within testate amoebae and it is not necessary to know the exact genus or species for wastewater microscopy practical application purposes, rather just that it is a "tes-

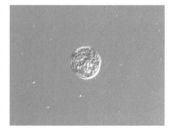

Figure 5.3 Testate amoebae cropped from 200x DIC

tate amoeba". It is common to see low amounts of testate amoebae present; however they often proliferate when there are high amounts of particulate BOD (food) available. Note that an added potential for "stress" is cell lysis, in which upon death bacteria release their contents and create particulate material from their broken-up cellular matter (Jenkins et al., 2004). When testate amoebae are the predominant higher life form organism, concern is not always warranted, however if testate amoebae are predominant, higher amounts of particulate BOD (and the potential for stress) may warrant further investigation (Kosakyan and Lara, 2019).

5.4 Free Swimming Ciliates

Free swimming ciliates are generally round, ranging from 20-400µm in dimension and they achieve motility through rows of short, hair-like cilia (Mountain Empire Community College, n.d-a). There is high genetic diversity within free swimming ciliates, however classification beyond "free swimming ciliate" is not needed for practical applications in wastewater treatment processes. Some free-swimming ciliates may also have cilia that may infuse as "spikes" allowing them to attach to floc surfaces and graze, acting as crawling ciliates. Ciliates, in general, are sensitive to many environmental stresses so their presence can often be an indication of good general health. There has been no successful linking of free-swimming ciliates to sludge age conditions. In general, free-swimming ciliates appear in slightly more mature systems in which there are lesser amounts of prey density of dispersed single cell bacteria.

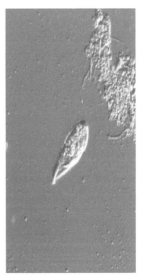

Figure 5.4 free swiming ciliate cropped 200x DIC cropped 200x DIC

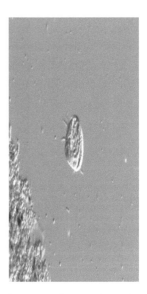

Figure 5.5 free swimmnig_ crawling ciliate cropped from 200x DIC

5.5 Stalked Ciliates

Stalked or "attached" ciliates occur under similar conditions as free swimming ciliates, however they differentiate by attaching to the flocs through stalks. Stalked ciliates can exist as individual or colonial microorganisms. Stalked ciliates eat through a process called phagocytosis in which the plasma membrane of the cell is used to engulf large food particles, creating vacuoles (basically the "stomach" mechanism). The food follows a path in which it is broken down by lysosomes, and when small enough, food then enters the membrane of the cell. Excess food that remains after the metabolism process is then excreted (Mountain Empire Community College, n.d-a).

Most stalked ciliates are heterotrophs that feed on small bacteria and other debris. Typically, stalked ciliate types use their cilia to filter or sweep in their food. The cilia then direct this food through the mouth and into the gullet where the vacuoles are then formed for the metabolism process. Other types of stalked ciliates may have different feeding methods such as absorption, or cannibalistic methods where they feed on other ciliates and higher life-form organisms rather than bacteria (Wikipedia, 2021c). There is high diversity within stalked ciliates (thousands of taxonomic classifications), however from a wastewater microscopy perspective identification beyond "stalked ciliate" is not necessary. The predominance of stalked ciliates is generally considered a sign of good overall health and usually (but not always) good sludge quality.

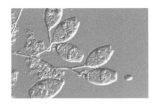

Figure 5.6 stalked ciliates 200x DIC

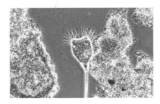

Figure 5.7 suctorian cropped 100x phase

Figure 5.8 vaginicola 200x DIC cropped

Figure 5.9 colonial stalked ciliates 200x DIC

5.6 Rotifers

Rotifers are more complex than protozoan (classified as metazoan) and exist in a wide range of shapes and sizes. The taxonomic classification of rotifers is currently in flux, however, it is generally accepted that over 2,000 species of rotifers exist. Most rotifers are motile but may also attach to flocs. Rotifers feed on small particulate matter such as dead bacteria, protozoan, and other particulate organic material. In practical experience, we have cited the presence of rotifers in SRT values of 3-4 days so therefore it is not considered good practice to attempt to correlate rotifers with SRT values. More accurately, rotifers appear to predominate when there is an abundance of "rotifer food". Rotifer's preferred substrate in wastewater appears to generally be pin floc or "broken up" floc material. In lagoon wastewater treatment processes, many rotifers are algal predators (Richard, 2003).

Figure 5.10 rotifer cropped from 200x DIC

Female rotifers are generally larger than male rotifers (up to 10x larger) and in most species, males lack digestive systems, causing them to have very short life spans with the almost sole purpose of mating (Wikipedia 2021b). (Chances are that if you are viewing a rotifer under the microscope, it is a female.) In nature the lifespan of a female rotifer typically ranges from two days to three weeks. Reproduction methods vary depending on rotifer species, with females producing shelled eggs which may either attach to other material or in some species the female may carry the eggs inside their body until they hatch.

The body of a rotifer is divided into a head, trunk, and foot. The most recognized and distinguished feature of rotifers (female rotifers) is the corona on the head (Mountain Empire Community College, n.d.-b). Depending on the species, there is some configuration of cilia around the mouth which then enter the mastax (where the "food" is chewed). Rotifers also have stomachs, a nervous system, two pairs of antennae, and up to 5 eyes. Mucus secreted by rotifers at the mouth, or the foot is believed to help aid in floc formation. Rotifers, while generally much "hardier" than ciliates are still strict aerobes and can die when threshold levels of stress occur (Bitton, 2005).

5.7 Nematodes

Nematodes are metazoans commonly found in wastewater treatment processes in small numbers (Rumbaugh, 2018). It is believed that nematodes typically enter wastewater treatment processes through attachment to soil associated with inflow and infiltration. Most nematodes found in wastewater treatment plants are typically 2-3 microns in length and prey on floc particles and bacteria, such as fecal bacteria.

Figure 5.11 nematode cropped from 200x DIC

Nematodes are aerobic organisms, and their growth is inhibited in anoxic and anaerobic environments (Wikipedia, 2021d). While nematodes tend to be found more frequently in systems with higher sludge retention times, we don't recommend trying to correlate them to sludge age, food to microorganism ratio, or use their presence or absence as the basis for any operational control adjustments. We have analyzed mixed liquor samples with sludge ages of under 3 days in which nematodes are present.

We have also observed high amounts of nematodes briefly in mixed liquor systems shortly after final clarifiers are taken offline and cleaned out and suspect they may inhabit the sludge blankets or grow on the walls of the clarifiers.

Nematodes have many unique characteristics such as no stomach muscles. Rather food moves through the digestive system as a result of body movements. Others have teeth and stylets which can be thrust into their prey. Reproduction varies between sexual reproduction or self-fertilization of eggs by hermaphrodite species (Encyclopedia Britannica, n.d.-b).

From a practical standpoint it is worth noting the presence of nematodes under the microscope, however their presence is common, beneficial in many instances (trickling filters etc.), and nothing that would typically warrant additional concern.

5.8 Water Bear (Tardigrade)

Alternate names for Tardigrades include "water bears" or "moss piglets" (thanks to an episode of the South Park TV show). The name Tardigrade originated from a Spanish translation of "slow stepper". There are approximately 1,300 known species of water bear within the phylum Tardigrada which is believed to have originated over 500 million years ago. Tardigrades are famous for their extreme adaptability and may perhaps be nature's most durable creature (Bradford and Weisberger, 2021). Water bears have been known to adapt to extreme temperatures and a wide range of environmental conditions including mountains, volcanos, the Antarctic, and have even survived in outer space (The Smithsonian, 2021). According to Smithsonian

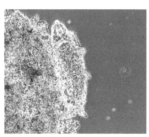

Figure 5.12:Waterbear 100x phase contrast

magazine, tardigrades can withstand environments as cold as minus 328 degrees Fahrenheit (minus 200 Celsius) or highs of more than 300 degrees F (148.9 C). Water bears may also survive radiation, boiling liquids, and even massive amounts of pressure (The Smithsonian, 2021).

Water bears have eight legs with claws and a gait (head) that resembles a bear. The mouth of the water bear has hard "stylets", which it uses to pierce its prey and suck the contents out. The skin is transparent, and it is often possible to view the contents of what a water bear has recently eaten (Encyclopedia Britanica, n.d.-c). The normal lifespan of a water bear in nature (uninterrupted by stressful conditions) is anywhere from 3-4 months to a little over 2 years. Water bears have a unique ability through a process called cryptobiosis to enter a "tun" state, in which they can suspend their metabolism for up to 10 years or longer when exposed to stressful conditions. When conditions again become conductive to normal life functions they simply reanimate and resume their life functions within a matter of hours (Wikipedia, 2021f).

In wastewater processes, water bears may prey on bacteria, plant matter, algae, or may be carnivorous preying on nematodes and rotifers (Wikipedia, 2021f). Some species of water bear are even known to be cannibalistic and prey on other water bear. From a practical standpoint in wastewater processes, the presence of water bear typically indicates a higher SRT value and low ammonia concentrations (i.e. good nitrification) as ammonia is a recognized stressor. From an operational standpoint, the presence or absence of water bear should not warrant any operational changes.

5.9 Gastrotrich

Gastrotrich are invertebrates occasionally found in wastewater treatment systems. Generally, their presence indicates good overall "health", and they tend to occur in systems with higher SRT values. There are approximately 500 species of Gastrotrich recognized within the phylum Gastrotricha, with species in nature occurring over a broad range of conditions (salt water, freshwater, soil, sandy seashores). Movement is achieved through cilia. Gastrotrich prey on bacteria, organic debris, and certain protozoa (Encyclopedia Britannica, n.d.-a). From an operational standpoint, the presence or absence of water bear should not warrant any operational changes.

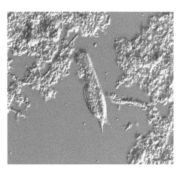

Figure 5.13 gastrotirch 200x DIC

5.10 Other Higher Invertebrates Occasionally Found in Wastewater Treatment Processes

From a practical standpoint the below higher invertebrate microorganisms tend to be found in fixed film systems or processes in which there are higher SRT values. The presence of these microorganisms is relatively incidental and generally not considered overly significant for wastewater treatment purposes.

5.10A Bristle Worms

The presence and significance of bristle worms in wastewater treatment plants is rather poorly understood and relatively insignificant. It is suspected that some of this may be due to the high genetic diversity of these organisms, more than 10,000 species (Wikipedia, 2021e). In practical applications bristle worms are often found in fixed film systems and systems with higher SRT values. Bristle worms are recognized by their bristles (chaetae) and generally have multiple sets of eyes. Often, when bristle worms are present at high abundance this may impact a red-pink tint (Leighton, n.d.).

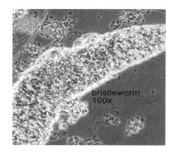

Figure 5.14 bristle worm 100x phase contrast

5.10B Crustaceans

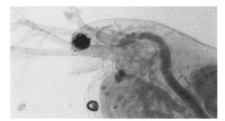

Figure 5.15 daphnia brightfield 4x

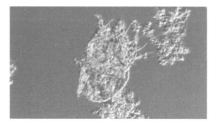

Figure 5.16 crustacean- water mite 200x DIC

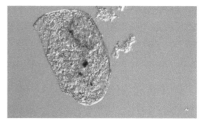

Figure 5.17 crustacean 200x DIC

- Daphnia
- Water Mites
- Other

5.10C Algae

- Cyanobacteria
- Diatoms
- Green algae

ALGAE TO BE DISCUSSED LATER IN THIS TEXTBOOK (LAGOON TREATMENT SECTION).

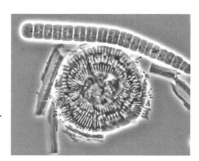

Figure 5.18 cyanobacteria filament and diatom

Chapter 6:

Higher Power Microscopy Observation Techniques

Figure 6.0 objective lenses

6.1 The "Hard Smash"

The most essential aspect of getting a good view at high power magnification under the scope is getting the sample as flat as possible. Because low power observations have already been conducted, diluting the sample does not have significant impact on the high-power magnification findings (with the exception that more than 1 slide may need to be viewed to thoroughly look at a minimum of 20-30 flocs) (M. Richard, personal communication, 2015). The amount of dilution water used may vary depending on many factors such as personal preference, allocated time, and if pictures from the sample are to be taken. The most important thing is to get as flat a surface as possible as "you cannot ID what you cannot see".

6.1A "Hard Smash" Procedure

- Dilute the mixed liquor sample as needed with water.
  - The most efficient dilutions tend to create a concentration of around 1500 mg/L mixed liquor.
- Place 1 well mixed drop (approximately 20 µL) towards the end of one side of a clean slide.
  - It may be good practice and save some resources to use two cover slips on each slide.
- Gently drop a cover slip over the mixed liquor sample.
  - Be sure to only use one cover slip as they can easily stick together.
- Using absorbent paper, gently press each edge of the cover slip to dispel any extra liquid.
- Once each edge is pressed rather gently, press forcefully (as hard as possible) on the cover slip.
  - Techniques may vary- I prefer using the lower part of my palm while standing over it.

NOTE THAT THE SURFACE USED FOR SLIDE PREPARATION MUST BE FLAT, OR IT IS VERY LIKELY THE SLIDE WILL BREAK. EVEN WITH A FLAT SURFACE OCCASIONALLY A SLIDE WILL BREAK. SIMPLY REPEAT WITH A FRESH SLIDE AND COVER SLIP.

6.2 Bringing a Sample into Focus

The majority of the high-power magnification findings is attributed to viewing of the sample at 1000x oil immersion. The procedure is as follows:

- Start with viewing the sample at 100x (10x lens) and using the phase 1 ring under the stage of the microscope.
- Once an object (preferably a floc) is in focus, increase to 20x and then 40x lens using corresponding phase adjustments to match the lens and refocus as needed.
- Toggle the lens between the 40x and the 100x and place one small drop of oil on the cover slip.
- Rotate the phase ring to match the 100x lens and slide the 100x lens over the cover slip.
- Using the fine adjustment knob, bring the sample into focus as needed.

SHOULD PROBLEMS IN THIS STEP ARISE, PLEASE REFER TO MICROSCOPIC FUNDAMENTALS, CHAPTER 3 OF THIS TEXT.

6.3 Steps to Identifying an Unknown Filament Type

Background

For practical wastewater microscopy purposes, it is important to note that we identify microbes by their physical characteristics (morphotype) which are then linked to various potential operational causes if the morphotype should reach significant abundance (ranked common or greater). Filamentous bacteria morphotypes have been successfully correlated to various operational conditions with a successful track record of >40 years and counting. At the time of this writing, we are in the midst of the process of learning more about the potential genetic diversity within various morphotypes and if and when this knowledge may potentially be applied to further our troubleshooting capabilities.

6.3A Diameter Measurement

Diameter is a critical component for filamentous morphotype analysis. Measuring the diameter can quickly reduce the list of possibilities. A reticle is needed in the eyepiece of the microscope for diameter measurement. When using the diagnostic table, it is recommended to use 1.0 μm as a "measuring stick," separating filaments as being thinner or thicker than 1.0 μm.

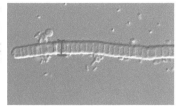

Figure 6.1 diameter

6.3B Presence/Absence of Septa (Cross-Walls)

Septa may be described as the visual separation between individual cells of a filament. If septa are visible, this may be noted and applied for morphotype identification. Most, but not all filament types have visible septa. Occasionally, septa may be present but not visible for reasons such as attached growth, quality of microscope etc.

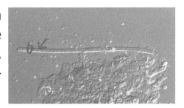

Figure 6.2 cross walls-septa

6.3C Presence/Absence of Intra-Cellular Sulfur Granules

Certain filament types have mixotrophic functions and may utilize sulfide as a source of growth. Intra-cellular sulfur granules may be viewed in filaments such as type 0914/0803 (square shape- all of the other types possess circular shaped granules), Thiothrix, Beggiatoa, and type 021N filament morphotypes. Sulfur granules typically appear as bright-yellow cell inclusions ("Christmas lights"). If sulfur granules are viewed within a filament the list of potential morphotype candidates is significantly reduced and it is known that sulfide is being utilized for growth (M. Richard, personal communication, 2004). Using the identification table, the presence of sulfur granules may be used using a "yes or no" answer.

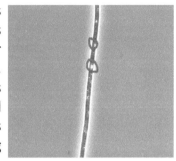

Figure 6.3 sulfur granules

IT IS IMPORTANT TO NOTE THAT THE ABOVE MORPHOTYPES MAY EXIST WITH OR WITHOUT THE PRESENCE OF INTRA-CELLULAR SULFUR GRANULES. BEING MIXOTROPHS, THESE FILAMENT TYPES MAY ALSO UTILIZE ORGANIC ACIDS AS SUBSTRATE (IN ADDITION TO SULFIDE) SO NOT SEEING SULFUR GRANULES DOES NOT RULE OUT THE MORPHOTYPE AS A POSSIBILITY.

6.3D Measurement of Cell Size/ Dimensions

Cell size is measured as the diameter by the length of the cell in μm.

Example #1

Cell shape is square. Cell diameter is 1 μm and cell length is 1 μm. *Cell size = 1μm x 1μm.*

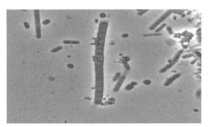

Figure 6.4 dimensions

Example #2

Cell shape is rectangular. Cell diameter is 1 μm and cell length is 3 μm. *Cell size = 1μm x 3μm.*

FOR FILAMENT CELLS WITHOUT VISIBLE CELL WALLS/SEPTA IT IS NOT POSSIBLE TO DETERMINE INDIVIDUAL CELL SIZE AND FOR THESE INSTANCES CELL DIMENSION IS NOT APPLICABLE.

6.3E Presence/Absence of a Sheath

Certain filament types contain a sheath. Sheaths may best be described as "peas in a pod" with the sheath being a "protective" layer in which the filamentous cells are encased in a protective covering.

- Sheaths are often easier to observe when an empty cell is present.
  - o Sometimes sheath's can be difficult to see so the absence of a sheath does not necessarily eliminate a filamentous morphotype from the identification.
  - o It is often useful to view similar filament types and look for a sheath rather than focus on one individual filament for this.

NOTE THAT WHEN USING PHASE CONTRAST, A "HALO" EFFECT MAY GENERATED AROUND THE FILAMENT. ANY "HALO'S" SHOULD NOT BE MISTAKEN FOR A SHEATH (JENKINS ET AL., 2004).

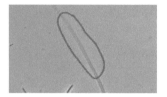

Figure 6.5 sheath empty

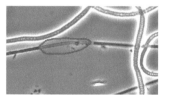

Figure 6.6 sheath

6.3F Cell Shapes

Cell Shape Options in the Identification Table

- Sausage
- Rectangle
- Discs, Ovals
- Elongated Rods
- Square
- Irregular/Barrell
- Oval Rods
- N/A (Not applicable/ no cell shape visible)

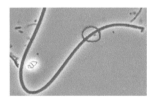

Figure 6.7 sausage

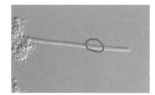

Figure 6.8 rectangle

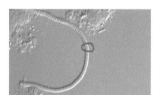

Figure 6.9 discs ovals

Figure 6.10 elongated

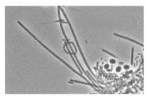

Figure 6.11 square

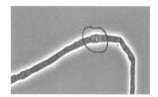

Figure 6.12 irregular

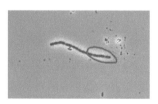

Figure 6.13 oval rods

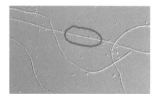

Figure 6.14 no septa

6.3G Other Morphology Traits of Note

Additional Morphology Traits

- True Branching
- False Branching
- "Transparent" Appearance
- "Bundles or Twisted Ropes"
- "Pins in a pin-cushion"
- PHB Granules
- Attached Growth

Figure 6.15 true branching

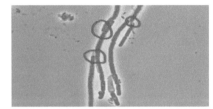
Figure 6.16 false branching

Figure 6.17 transparent

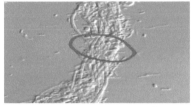
Figure 6.18 bundles_twisted ropes

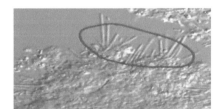
Figure 6.19 pins in a pincushion

Figure 6.20 PHB granules

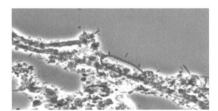
Figure 6.21 attached growth

6.4 Filament Morphotype Identification Table

The table below is compatible with a bench sheet that may be used to identify filamentous bacteria by recognized morphotypes. Please note that due to high potential for genetic diversity within the morphotypes as well as factors such as growth rates, substrate utilized, and more, there may be some variation between "textbook" and practical application.

IT IS OK FOR A FILAMENT TO BE RECOGNIZED AS "UNKNOWN". ONLY FILAMENT TYPES THAT ARE COMMONLY RESPONSIBLE FOR BULKING EVENTS ARE LISTED WITHIN THIS TABLE.

Identification Table for Common Filamentous Morphotypes observed in Activated Sludge

Filament Morphotype	Notes	Filament Diameter (Typical values)	Septa/ Cell Walls observed y/n	Can store sulfide (potential for sulfur granules)	Cell Shape/Size (Size= diameter by cell length) μm	Sheath y/n
Sphaerotilus	Commonly has false branching.	1.2-2.6 μm	Yes	No	Sausage shaped. 1.6 x 2.5	Yes
Type 1701	Thinner filament with sausage shaped cells (sometimes cells are hard to see). Occasionally has attached growth.	0.8- 1.0 μm	Yes- Usually.	No	Sausage shaped. 1.0 x 1.5	Yes
Haliscomenobacter	0.5 um diameter (skinny) Often "pins in a pin cushion". Sheath often difficult to see.	0.5 μm	No- Usually.	No	Usually can't see individual cells. Occasionally small sausage shaped cells are visible.	yes
Type 021N	Large filament that typically extends from the flocs or bridges flocs together. Irregular cell shape.	1.6-2.5 μm	Yes	Yes	Barrels, rectangles, discoid. 1.6 X 2.5	No
Thiothrix	Rectangular cell shape. Typically extends from flocs.	0.8- 2.8 μm	Yes	Yes	Rectangles. 0.8-1.4 x 1.0-3.0	Yes
Type 0914/0803	Occasionally has square sulfur granules.	1.0-1.2 μm	Yes	Yes	Square. 1.0 x 1.0	Yes
Beggiatoa	Typically motile and usually contains either sulfur granules or PHB granules.	2.0- 4.0 μm	Sometimes.	Yes	Rectangles. 2.0-4.0 x 6.0 -8.0	No
Nostocoida limicola I and II	"Hockey pucks".	0.8-2.0 μm	Yes	No	Discs, ovals. 0.8 x 1.0-1.5	No
Nostocoida limicola III	Individual discoid cells.	1.7-2.5 μm	Yes	No	Discs, Ovals 2.0 x 1.5	No
Type 0411	"Elongated rods/ long sausage links".	0.8-1.2 μm	Yes	No	Sausage, Rods. 0.8-1.2 x 2.0-5.0	No
Type 0961	Transparent/ "lighter" appearance.	1.0-1.4 μm	Yes	No	Rectangles. 1.0-1.4 x 2.0-4.0	No (not a true sheath).
Type 0092	Neisser positive. Need Neisser stain to ID. Often difficult to see at phase contrast.	0.6-1.2 μm	Yes- Sometimes but not always.	No	Rectangles. 0.8-1.0 x 1.0 (Common to not see individual cells).	No (not a true sheath).
Type 0041/0675	"Grainy" appearance. Often has attached growth.	1.0-2.2 μm	Yes	No	Squares. 1.0-2.0 x 2.0-3.0	Yes
Type 1851	Often forms "bundles/twisted ropes". Often has attached growth.	0.8 μm- 1 μm	Often difficult to view septa.	No	Rectangles. Generally 0.8 x 1.4 ballpark.	Yes

Microthrix	Gram positive. Often has Neisser positive granules. Typically "coiled".	0.5-0.8μm	Very rarely see septa	No	Typically can't see individual cells	No
Actinomycetes-Mycolata	"True branching". Almost all species in wastewater stain gram positive when healthy.	0.8-1.2μm	Yes- most species.	No	Variable. 1.0 x 1.0- 2.0	No
Type 1863	Usually dispersed. "Chain of cells" appearance.	0.8-1.0 μm	Yes	No	Oval rods. 0.8-1.0 x 1.0-1.5	No
Type 0211	Grows dispersed. "Thin and crooked".	0.3-0.4 μm	Yes	No	Oval rods. 0.4 x 0.6	No
Type 0581	Looks like *Microthrix* but gram positive.	0.5-0.8 μm	No	No	_____	No
Fungi	Very Large/True branching.	5.0-10.0 μm	Sometimes.	No	Variable.	No (but does often have thick cellulose cell wall).

6.5 Filamentous Morphotypes and Commonly Associated Causes

Filament Type	Potential Cause (s)
Sphaerotilus	• Low Dissolved Oxygen Concentrations.
Type 1701	• Low Dissolved Oxygen Concentrations.
Haliscomenobacter	• Various- In most instances N/A. -see 6.5A
Type 021N	• Elevated concentrations of low molecular weight organic acids. • Sulfide.
Type 0914/0803	• Elevated concentrations of low molecular weight organic acids. • Sulfide.
Thiothrix	• Elevated concentrations of low molecular weight organic acids. • Sulfide.
Beggiatoa	• Elevated concentrations of low molecular weight organic acids. • Sulfide.
Type 0411	• Elevated concentrations of low molecular weight organic acids.
Type 0211	• Elevated concentrations of low molecular weight organic acids.
Nostocoida limicola (I and II)	• Elevated concentrations of low molecular weight organic acids.
Nostocoida limicola III	• Elevated concentrations of low molecular weight organic acids. • Low phosphorous availability.
Type 0961	• Elevated concentrations of low molecular weight organic acids.
Type 0581	• Elevated concentrations of low molecular weight organic acids.
Type 0092	• Elevated concentrations of low molecular weight organic acids.
Type 1851	• Elevated Sludge Retention Time Values.
Type 0675/0041	• Elevated Sludge Retention Time Values.
Microthrix	• Fats, Oils, and Grease (Long chain fatty acids).
Actinomycetes-Mycolata	• Long Chain Fatty Acids. ○ Often, but not always formed from septic fats, oils, and grease.
Type 1863	• Fats, Oils, and Grease.

6.5A Additional Notes and Theories Related to Various Morphotypes (R. Hennessy and M. Richard, Personal Communications)

Filament type	Notes/ Theories
Haliscomenobacter	Since the discovery of this morphotype, various potential causes have been suggested. Due to high potential genetic diversity within the filament type, we generally do not attempt to correlate causes of Haliscomenobacter to plant conditions without comparison of operational data. Potential causes include: • Low dissolved oxygen concentrations • Low phosphorous availability • "Stress" • Difficult to degrade organics/ high COD: BOD ratio • Insignificant (non-bulking) filaments associated with the Chloroflexi phylum (generally occur at higher SRT values)
Beggiatoa	Rarely found in activated sludge systems/ most often associated with fixed film processes. Occasionally observed in lagoon systems (suspected that attached growth may occur in various areas of the lagoon or collection system). Generally associated with higher F/M ratio in initial contact zone.
Nostocoida limicola III	Often associated with high F/M ratio in the initial contact zone of the aeration basin in addition to proliferation at elevated organic acid concentrations.
Type 0411	Often Associated with high F/M ratio in the initial contact zone of the aeration basin in addition to proliferation at elevated organic acid concentrations.
Type 0211	Has commonly been observed in systems that accept septic tank holding waste. Generally, they tend to occur in areas of high F/M ratio (or likely grow in "side-stream" processes).
Type 0961	While the recognized growth cause is elevated organic acid concentrations, this filament is often found in systems with higher SRT values.
Type 0581	Of all of the filaments listed on the table, filament type 0581 appears to be the least viewed (based on samples from thousands of plants). Elevated organic acid concentrations are the recognized growth cause, and this filament type appears to favor plants with a high SRT value and increased periods of time in which septicity of the RAS may occur.
Type 0092	Filament type 0092 appears to be most commonly viewed in systems with coupled anaerobic-aerobic systems or enhanced biological nutrient removal systems with anaerobic selector zones favoring higher SRT values.
Type 1851	Many of the genera that may possess type 1851 morphology may store sugars under anaerobic conditions in addition to occurring at higher SRT values.
Type 0675/0041	Generally associated with a low F/M ratio on the back end of the aeration basin/biological process in addition to higher SRT values.
Type 1863	Filament type 1863 appears to be correlated with recent fats, oils, and grease entering a wastewater treatment process. It is theorized that type 1863 generally grows in the collection system and enters wastewater treatment processes through the influent.
Actinomycetes-Mycolata	From a genetic standpoint, there are thousands of potential genera and species that may possess Actinomycetes-Mycolata morphology. Potential causes include: • Fats, Oils, and Grease (generally "food based"). • Long chain fatty acids- often, but not always fats, oils, and grease related. • "Stress". • Difficult to degrade materials/ a High COD:BOD ratio. GENERALLY IN MUNICIPAL SYSTEMS FATS, OILS, AND GREASE ARE SUSPECTED WHILE IN INDUSTRIAL PROCESSES IT IS COMMON FOR ACTINOMYCETES FILAMENT TYPES TO GROW DUE TO OTHER CAUSES.

6.6 Compatible Bench Sheet for Identification Table Usage

Filamentous Bacteria Identification Bench Sheet
(Compatible with Identification Table)

Sample Date_____
Observation Date_____
Sample ID_____
Lab Tech Name_____

Filament #	1	2	3	4	5	6
Diameter, μm						
Septa?						
Sulfur granules?						
Cell Shape*						
Cell Size, μm						
Sheath?						
Abundance (1-6)						
Identification						

Notes
- **Cell Shape Options:** Sausage, Rod, Barrell, Discoid/Disc, Oval, Rectangular, Square, N/A, Variable
- **Gram positive:** Microthrix and Actinomycetes-Mycolata filament types
- **Neisser positive:** Filament type 0092, Polyphosphate Accumulating Organisms
- **Cell size=** Diameter by length

ALL OTHER GRAM AND NEISSER STAINING REACTIONS BESIDES THOSE LISTED ABOVE ARE INSIGNIFICANT FOR FILAMENT MORPHOTYPE IDENTIFICATION

6.6A Ranking Filament Abundance (Jenkins et al., 2004)

Value	Abundance	Description
0	None	No filaments observed.
1	Few	Low/insignificant filaments observed.
2	Some	Per average floc viewed <5 filaments are observed.
3	Common	Per average floc viewed 5 filaments are observed.
4	Very Common	Per average floc viewed 5-20 filaments are observed.
5	Abundant	Per average floc viewed >20 filaments are observed.
6	Excessive	There appears to be a higher % of filaments than flocculated bacteria.

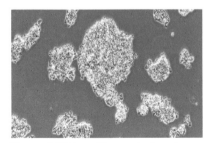

Figure 6.22 low filament abundance 100x phase

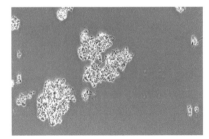

Figure 6.23 common filaments 100x phase

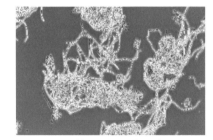

Figure 6.24 filaments abundant 100x phase

6.7 Gram and Neisser Staining

Background

In practical application, the majority of filamentous bacteria morphotype identification is accomplished at phase contrast, oil immersion, 1000x magnification. While staining reactions have been de-emphasized to adjust to factors such as genetic diversity amongst filament types and other chemistry reactions in various industrial wastewater processes, it is still necessary to perform staining for a complete and thorough microscopic evaluation.

Practical Application

In addition to certain staining attributes necessary for certain morphotype identification, it is also often easy to underestimate filament abundance or perhaps not see certain filaments in the absence of staining when using phase contrast. (An argument can be made here for DIC microscopy in addition to phase contrast however from a logistical standpoint these microscopes are generally not cost effective in wastewater applications).

6.7A Gram Stain

Preparation

- Using a representative mixed liquor sample pipette approximately 20 µL onto the right corner of a slide.
- Using the side of the pipette, spread the sample evenly (to the left) covering approximately 75% of the total slide.
- It is beneficial to label the slide on the left-hand side (slides with frosted edges are especially convenient for this).
- Allow time for the slide to air dry (generally around 10-15 minutes).

NOTE: IT OFTEN SAVES TIME TO START THE MICROSCOPIC EVALUATION WITH THE PREPARATION OF THE SLIDES BEING STAINED TO ALLOW ADEQUATE DRYING TIME.

Procedure

- Cover the slide by applying stain #1 (crystal violet reagent).
  - o Allow the reagent to sit for approximately 60 seconds.
  - o Rinse slide (both sides) with water.
- Cover the slide by applying stain #2 (iodine reagent).
  - o Allow reagent to sit for approximately 60 seconds.
  - o Rinse slide (both sides) with water.
- Hold the slide at an angle and decolorize with reagent #3 (decolorizer).
  - o Add decolorizer drop by drop for approximately 25 seconds (or until the liquid dispelled from the slide is clear).
- Cover the slide by applying reagent #4 (safarin).
  - o Allow the reagent to sit for approximately 60 seconds.
  - o Rinse slide (both sides) with water.
- Place slide on a piece of paper towel and blot dry with an absorbent paper.

Application

- Adjust the phase condenser to the brightfield setting.
- Place slide on microscope stage.
- Add a drop of oil to slide (no cover slip is used in any stains).
- Focus at 1000x magnification and view sample.

Results

- Gram Positive= Purple
- Gram Negative= Red

DR. MICHAEL RICHARD SUGGESTS THAT MOST FLOC FORMING BACTERIA ARE GRAM NEGATIVE, WHILE GRAM POSITIVE BACTERIA ARE GENERALLY RELATED TO SEPTICITY/ORGANIC ACIDS, AND/OR FATS, OILS, AND GREASE.

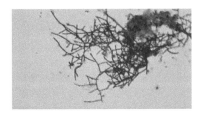

Figure 6.25 Actinomycetes-Mycolata Gram positive

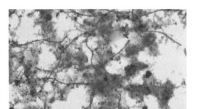

Figure 6.26 Gram negative

6.7B Neisser Stain

Preparation

- Using a representative mixed liquor sample, pipette approximately 20 µL onto the right corner of a slide.
- Using the side of the pipette, spread the sample evenly (to the left) covering approximately 75% of the total slide.
- It is beneficial to label the slide on the left-hand side (slides with frosted edges are especially convenient for this).
- Allow time for the slide to air dry (generally around 10-15 minutes).

Procedure

- Cover the slide by applying stain #1 (crystal violet and methylene blue mixture).
  - Allow the reagent to sit for approximately 30 seconds.
  - Rinse slide (both sides) with water.
- Cover the slide by applying stain #2 (Bismark brown reagent).
  - Allow reagent to sit for approximately 60 seconds.
  - Rinse slide (both sides) with water.
- Place the slide on a piece of paper towel and blot dry with an absorbent paper.

Application

- Adjust the phase condenser to the brightfield setting.
- Place the slide on the microscope stage.
- Add a drop of oil to slide (no cover slip is used in any stains).
- Focus at 1000x magnification and view sample.

Results

- Neisser positive= Purple
- Neisser Negative= Brown

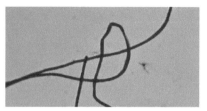

Figure 6.27 Nostocoida limicola III Neisser positive

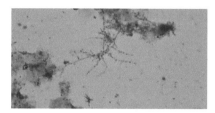

Figure 6.28 Actinomycetes_Mycolata Neisser negative with Neisser positive Granules 1000x

6.8 Additional High-Power Microscopy Morphotypes of Importance

Associated Cause	Morphotype
Elevated Organic Acid Concentrations	Spirilla
	Flexibacter
	Spirochaetes
	Microscrilla
	Tetrads
	Zoogloea
C1 Compounds (i.e. Methanol)	Hyphomicrobium
"Stress" (various potential causes)	"Irregular Growth Formations" (often star-fish-like).

NOTE THAT SOME (BUT NOT ALL) GENERA/SPECIES CAPABLE OF POSSESSING FLEXIBACTER, SPIROCHAETES, MICROSCRILLA, AND SPIRILLA MORPHOLOGY MAY BE MICROAEROPHILIC (ABLE TO COMPETE IN EXTREMELY LOW DISSOLVED OXYGEN CONDITIONS) (DUEHOLM ET AL. 2021).

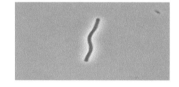

Figure 6.29 Spirillium cropped from 1000x phase contrast

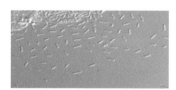

Figure 6.30 Flexibacter

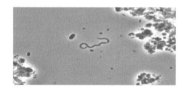

Figure 6.31 Spirochaetes cropped 1000x phase

Figure 6.32 Microscrilla DIC cropped 1000x

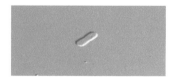

Figure 6.33 Flexibacter cropped from 1000x DIC

Figure 6.34 tetrads cropped 1000x phase contrast

Figure 6.35 zoogloea cropped from 1000x DIC

Figure 6.36 Hyphomicrobium phase

Figure 6.37 irregular growth formations phase contrast

6.9 Fluorescent Microscopy Viability Applications

Background

Our opinion is that fluorescent viability microscopy adds significant value to a microscopy assessment, and it is personally included in all microscopy evaluations. Unfortunately, the cost for a fluorescent microscope and the necessary reagents to perform this assay (generally >$15,000) are usually not logistical for in-house testing. Should viability testing be requested, sending a sample to a professional with this equipment is likely the most logistical strategy.

ATP (Adenosine triphosphate) testing is commonly used in boiling water applications to detect the presence of dead or alive bacteria. While a certain percentage of treatment plants have found ATP testing beneficial in wastewater, personal experience is that the majority of plants that have attempted ATP testing have not been able to effectively implement it as a tool for process control decisions. Our belief is that fluorescent microscopy is the most practical method for the level of detail needed for wastewater process control applications. Note that other viability testing applications such as flow cytometry may also be suitable options for specific applications (University of Toronto, n.d).

An important consideration in wastewater microscopy applications is the significant factor of variables that exist within the mixed liquor suspended solids (MLSS) concentration. The MLSS concentration includes factors such as inert/non-viable solids presence, higher life form organisms (up to 5-20% of MLSS by dry weight), polysaccharide, and bacteria (viable and non-viable) (Jenkins et al., 2004). In addition to these factors, parameters such as temperature may also have significant impact on the metabolic activity rates and the efficiency of bacteria for treatment.

While in-house analytical testing for MLSS concentrations is always good practice and always recommended it has also been proven with over 40 years of operational practice in large part thanks to the efforts by pioneers such as Dr. David Jenkins, Dr. Michael Richard, and Dick Eickelboom, that "the bugs don't lie" and when microscopy is performed correctly it is an irreplaceable operational tool.

6.9A Viability Components

Using a fluorescent microscope and an Invitrogen live/dead ™ BacLight ™ Bacterial Viability Kit, reagents may be prepared and 100 µL of mixed liquor sample in addition to 50 µL of prepared reagent are mixed in a small (1.5 mL) microcentrifuge tube. Upon approximately 15 minutes of mixture (in a dark environment) 20 µL may be placed on a slide with a cover slip and viewed using fluorescent microscopy.

6.9B Notes for Viability Fluorescent Microscopy Testing

There is inherently some subjectivity associated with this test method (similar to the Reverse India ink stain in this regard). It is important to view a minimum of 20-30 flocs and results may be interpreted as the % viability per average floc observed with notes included in instances where perhaps viability fluctuates significantly between flocs, or something like "a relatively equal mixture of flocs with high viability and low viability were observed" (Thermo Fisher Scientific, n.d.).

Procedure Notes and Interpretation of Results
- Press down on the cover slip in the same manner as the "hard smash" (a technique described earlier in this chapter).
- Begin with the 10x lens and also view the sample at 40x and 100x (oil immersion needed for 100x).

Results

- Green= Alive/Viable
- Red= Dead/Non-Viable
- Yellow= Interference
    - Interference can often be minimized by keeping the light source for the microscope and the surrounding environment as dark as possible.

Practical Application

Using this fluorescent testing method, we have found that target viability percentage may be highly specific to each individual plant. In general, it appears that a viability range of 40-70% most often correlates with good quality sludges and viability percentages below 40% or above 85% are more often found in problem systems. In general, filamentous bacteria tend to be healthy with lesser viability percentages observed within the interior of the flocs.

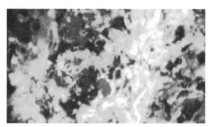

Figure 6.41 high viability 1000x

Below 35% viability, further investigation of inhibition or toxicity may often be warranted, while in systems with over 85% viability, it is theorized that the bacteria are growing at high or potentially logarithmic rates, which often is problematic for floc formation (most plants tend to operate best at the very start of the decline of the bacterial growth curve) (Wang et al., 2015).

In practical experience fluorescent viability microscopy has also been beneficial for applications such as RAS chlorination to selectively kill problematic filamentous bacteria.

Figure 6.42 low viability 1000x

Chapter 7:

Troubleshooting Tips and Strategies for Filamentous Bacteria Control

Introduction

This chapter will mirror problems discussed in Chapter 2 with potential operational control strategies for consideration. The level and time for which each operational intervention may be warranted is dependent on the logistics of each individual situation and can differ significantly depending on each plant as well as its treatment objectives. This text will only focus predominantly on changes that can be made at an operational level. It is important to note that there are limits to success through these methods and in some instances, engineering upgrades and/or implementation of reliable equipment/ infrastructure may be necessary to maintain a stable wastewater treatment operation process. Diagnosing problems through microscopy and other complimentary tools is often the "easy part", while using the information obtained through microscopy for operational control may be more challenging in many instances.

7.1 Filamentous Bulking Control Strategies Based on Causes

Figure: 7.1 clarifier failure

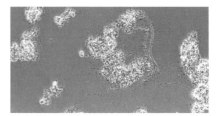

Figure: 7.2 bulking abundant filaments 100x phase

Background

As discussed in Chapter 2, filamentous bacteria, while beneficial at moderate levels within the floc, have the potential to contribute to elevated SVI values (poor settling). For effective solids-liquid separation in the final clarifier(s) the mixed liquor must settle/compact quickly enough that suspended solids are not lost over the clarifier weirs. In severe bulking instances, the sludge blanket in the clarifier overflows into the clarifier effluent. Elevated levels of suspended solids leaving the final clarifier(s) may contribute to issues such as elevated effluent TSS (total suspended solids), and elevated phosphorous concentrations in the final effluent. (Most bacteria in wastewater represented by total suspended solids make up roughly 2-3% weight by phosphorous so increased effluent TSS also leads to increased effluent total phosphorous concentrations) (Wisconsin Department of Natural Resources, 2016b). For plants that have tertiary filtration downstream of final clarifier processes, increased solids loss in clarifiers leads to an increasing frequency of filter fouling/ backwashing, sometimes with the potential to "overwhelm" the tertiary filtration process in which backwashing cannot be completed quickly enough to keep up with hydraulic flows.

Applications

Control strategies for filamentous bulking differ based on each individual circumstance (plant specific) depending on logistics. Microscopic evaluation should determine the filament morphotype(s) most responsible for bulking as well as reasonable speculation of their associated growth conditions. In this section common troubleshooting methods will be documented based on filamentous bulking causes.

7.1A Low DO Filamentous Bacteria

Low DO Defined

It is important to understand the concept of low dissolved oxygen. The easiest way to visualize this concept is picturing that when we measure DO in the aeration basin we are measuring "residual DO", but this does not account for depletion of oxygen as it penetrates the flocs. For example, if the oxygen uptake rate is high Figure 7.2 type 1701 cropped from 1000x phase contrast enough, 2 mg/L may be used up rapidly not leaving any additional DO available to penetrate deeper within the floc. Therefore, the term "low DO" is relative and very often the higher the oxygen uptake rate of the

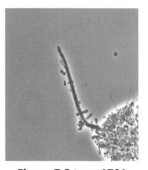

Figure 7.3 type 1701 cropped from 1000x

bacteria, the more DO is needed to discourage the growth of low DO filaments. Target DO concentrations of 2-3 mg/L are common setpoints in municipal processes, however the actual needed DO setpoint may be specific to each plant (either higher or lower) (Jenkins et al., 2004).

Common Troubleshooting Options for Low DO Filaments

- Increase the target DO setpoint or the amount of DO that is supplied to the aeration basin.
- Decrease the oxygen uptake rate of the bacteria by:
  - o reducing the organic loading rate (if possible)
  - o increasing the MLSS concentration to reduce the bacterial growth rates (and the oxygen uptake indirectly) (Richard, 2003).

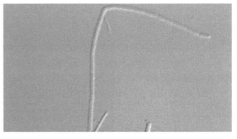
Figure: 7.4 Sphaerotilus 1000x DIC

  - It is not always true that "more bugs use more DO". Often, increasing MLSS concentration may reduce the growth rates of the bacteria (however clarifier solids loading rates and SVI values must be taken into consideration).
- Settling Aids (Polymer, Coagulants etc.):
  - o Consult chemical vendor for jar testing/ assistance.
- Selective Chlorination:
  - o See section later in this chapter about selective chlorination methods such as RAS chlorination to control filaments.

Other Considerations for Low DO Filaments (Site Specific and Additional Notes)

- Implementation of step-feed configuration, in which influent wastewater is fed to multiple parts along the aeration basin to spread out the oxygen demand more evenly.
- Putting an additional basin online (to distribute loading more evenly).
- Increase the RAS rate (allowing for a higher MLSS and lower F/M ratio at the front end of the aeration basin).
- Increase internal recycle flow rate to the anoxic zone (for BNR plants that may apply) to provide more nitrate as an available oxygen source as well as a source to dilute incoming organic acids.
- Increase the MLSS concentration by adding other bacteria (i.e. fresh WAS from a nearby treatment plant).
  - o See above for risk involved with increasing MLSS concentrations. Often chlorination is needed in conjunction with increasing the MLSS concentration to "knock down" filaments while also helping to alleviate the root cause for their growth.
- Modification from plug flow to complete mix process if applicable (to create conditions in which oxygen uptake rates are similar throughout all areas of the aeration basin and spread the loading more evenly).
- Other (if possible)
  - o Implementation/ Optimization of the Selector Zone through methods such as ORP monitoring.

Power Outages

Should power outages occur, experience (based on Dr. Richard's observations) has indicated that at >24-36 hours without dissolved oxygen deterioration of the biomass may occur. Ideally if the power is lost and aeration is not available, no influent loading should also occur. Influent loading in combination with lack of DO significantly increases the ability of septicity/low dissolved oxygen concentrations to have negative impact on the bacteria that compete.

7.1B Filaments That Proliferate at Elevated Concentrations of Low Molecular Weight Organic Acids

Understanding the Concept of Organic Acids

To understand the concept of organic acids, it is beneficial to look at the different basic types of BOD (food/substrate).

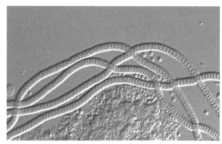

Figure: 7.5 Nostocoida limicola III cropped 1000x DIC

- Particulate
  - o Organic material in the form of solids. Solids are adsorbed (caught/attached) to the outside of the floc and enzymes break this material down in order for food to pass through the cell membrane ("mouth") (Absorption vs Adsorption, n.d.).
  - o A good analogy is the glycemic index for nutrition that we eat. This substrate (BOD) would be comparable to oatmeal (slow release- not highly readily available immediately).
  - o The more complex the organic material, the longer it takes for enzymes to make the food readily available for passage through the bacteria cell membrane.
- Soluble
  - o This food (BOD) is able to immediately pass through the cell membrane.
  - o Soluble substrate is readily available to be used by the bacteria. (Think "Kool-Aid" vs oatmeal in the above analogy).
    - Organic acids (or volatile acids) are a fraction of the soluble BOD which is most readily available for the bacteria.
      - Organic acids such as Acetic acid are commonly either oxidized or stored by bacteria within the first 30 minutes in the aeration basin (M. Richard, personal communication).

CERTAIN WASTEWATERS (PARTICULARLY INDUSTRIAL WASTEWATER PROCESSES) MAY BE NATURALLY HIGH IN ORGANIC ACIDS WHILE IN OTHER INSTANCES ORGANIC ACIDS MAY BE FORMED THROUGH SEPTICITY AND FERMENTATION REACTIONS.

Formation of Organic Acids Through Septicity and Fermentation

The majority of bacteria encountered in wastewater treatment are facultative in that they may utilize free DO or combined oxygen sources. It is rare for nitrate to be present in wastewater influents because nitrate is usually developed through nitrification. Some degree of septicity is always encountered prior to treatment due to the nature of carbonaceous material and lack of dissolved oxygen in areas such as collection systems, lift stations, eq basins etc. For facultative bacteria the order in which they use oxygen sources is:

1. Free Dissolved Oxygen.
2. Nitrate (use oxygen molecules and release nitrogen gas).
3. Sulfate (use oxygen molecules and reduce sulfate to sulfide) (Tyger, 2011).

Acid Forming Bacteria

Once all oxygen sources (free and combined) are depleted, the process of anaerobic treatment begins in which acid forming bacteria ferment/ "break down" longer chain carbonaceous material into shorter "smaller pieces"- organic acids. Due to the slow growth rates of methanogens and the necessary growth environments, it is rare for "full" anaerobic treatment to occur in areas of septicity. A useful way to visualize this concept is to view the formation of organic acids through septicity as "partial/incomplete" anaerobic treatment.

Common Areas in Which Organic Acids may be Formed

(Richard, 2003)

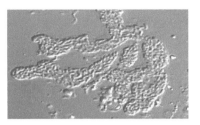

Figure: 7.6 fingered zoogloea DIC

- Collection Systems
- Lift Stations
- EQ Basins
- Primary Clarifiers
- Anaerobic/Anoxic Selector Cells
  - o In organically overloaded selector cells, if too many organic acids are not either oxidized or stored by bacteria in selector cells, the remaining organic acids pass into the aeration basin where they are readily available and have potential to significantly impact the bacteria that compete in the process.
  - o Organically underloaded selectors may also be problematic as once combined oxygen sources are depleted available carbon is not present to drive the ORP (oxidation reduction potential) low enough for the storage of substrate by organisms, such as polyphosphate accumulating organisms, while generation of organic acids still persists.
- Aeration basins in which the oxygen demand exceeds the available oxygen supplied resulting in depletion of free and combined oxygen.
- "Dead spots" in aeration basin in which aeration/mixing is not adequate resulting in settling of solids which eventually become septic and re-release organic acids upon cell lysis (benthic feedback).
- Final Clarifier(s)
  - o Septicity within the sludge blanket.
  - o Buildup of settled solids (often as the result of failed or uneven sludge scraper mechanisms.
- Side streams
  - o Solids handling liquid return
    - Centrate.
    - Filtrate from sludge dewatering.
    - Digester decant flow.
- Others
  - o Hauled in waste
    - Septage, leachate, etc.

Oxidation Reduction Potential (ORP)

ORP is a measurement conducted by an electrode (platinum based) that reflects the oxidizing and reducing potential of water as measured in mV. While there are a high number of complex variables involved in ORP measurement, from a septicity standpoint it is useful to view ORP in terms of positive and negative mV values (Fuller, 2016).

Positive vs. Negative ORP values

Dissolved oxygen probes are only able to measure "positive" oxygen values. Commonly, DO probes can read accurately to as low as 0.1-0.2 mg/L DO. When all free oxygen is depleted, ORP is a useful tool to measure "negative dissolved oxygen", in which the lower the ORP value, the more septic. Generally, as ORP values increase above zero, aerobic conditions are present, whereas if negative ORP values are measured facultative or anaerobic reactions occur (Fuller, 2016).

General ORP Values and Corresponding Biological Processes

- Organic Carbon Oxidation: +50 to +225 mV
- Nitrification: +100 to +300 mV
- Denitrification: +50 to -100 mV
- Organic Acid (VFA) storage and corresponding orthophosphate release (polyphosphate accumulating organisms): -200 to -400 mV
- Sulfide Formation: -50mV to -250 mV
- Acid formation (fermentation): -50mV to -225 mV
- Methane formation: -175 to -400mV or lower (Fuller, 2016).

Glycogen Accumulating Organisms (GAOs)

Functionality of GAOs in wastewater treatment processes remain poorly understood in addition to correlation with ORP values.

- Many GAOs are capable of nitrate reduction (Dueholm et al., 2021).
- GAOs are widely believed to compete with PAOs for substrate in enhanced biological phosphorous removal processes.
- Genera such as Ca Accumulibacter may act as either PAOs or GAOs depending on the (poorly understood) conditions (Dueholm et al., 2021).

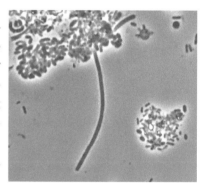

Figure: 7.7 GAOs cropped from 1000x Neisser

Septicity vs. Low DO

A useful way to view this (septicity vs. low DO) concept is to associate "septicity" with elevated concentrations of organic acids. Once organic acids are formed (under negative ORP values), they remain present, and it is typically only economical to oxidize organic acids through biological treatment. Note that oxidizing agents such as chlorine may raise the ORP value but are not effective in organic acid removal. (Once organic acids are there….they are there.)

Figure: 7.8 type 0411 cropped from 1000x phase contrast

If organic acids are present at high enough concentrations (generally >80 mg/L as total volatile acids,) this favors the growth of certain filamentous bacteria morphotypes. Filaments that proliferate at elevated organic acid concentrations are impartial to the amount of dissolved oxygen supplied in the aeration basin unless DO concentrations are low enough that fermentation reactions/generation of further organic acids may develop within the aeration basin. Therefore, if the DO is low enough/not adequate to reach the interior of the flocs, septicity may occur leading to organic acid formation, however once organic acids are present, increasing DO is not successful in oxidizing organic acids.

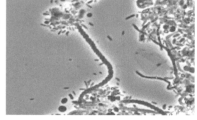

Figure: 7.9 Nostocoida limicola

An example of the concept above is if filamentous bulking is occurring due to excessive abundance of Nostocoida limicola filament types, changing the DO setpoint in the aeration basin is ineffective as the substrate allowing these filaments to compete is already present.

Common Control Strategies for Organic Acid Filamentous Bulking

Prevention/Reduction of Organic Acid Formation Through Chemical Methods

- If an area can be identified as a source of organic acid formation, several options exist to raise the ORP value preventing the formation of further organic acids, allowing the substrate (BOD) to enter the biological treatment in the form of more complex organic materials.
    - o Aeration
        - Keeping free dissolved oxygen available and ensuring positive ORP values.
    - o Hydrogen Peroxide
        - In addition to the oxidizing properties of hydrogen peroxide 1 lb. of peroxide also adds 0.5 lbs. of oxygen (M. Richard, Personal Communication).
    - o Calcium Nitrate
        - Nitrate is provided as an oxygen source to keep the ORP from decreasing below -75 mV. Bacteria utilize the nitrate as an oxygen source (denitrification reactions) (USP Technologies, 2021).
    - o * pH shock (high pH)
        - Some plants have found success with occasional high pH/caustic shock in areas such as the primary clarifier to inhibit the growth of acid forming bacteria (M Richard, personal communication).

Measures taken to reduce the HRT (Hydraulic Retention Time) in Problematic Areas.

These methods may have varying degrees of success but include:

- Increasing the frequency of pumping from lift stations (often by lowering the setpoint height in which the lead pump kicks on) to prevent the water from going stagnant/septic.
- In some instances, if high amounts of septicity are occurring in equalization basins, limiting the time the water is in the eq basin.
    - o This must be weighed against the overall organic loading rate as slug and shock loads are not conductive for maintaining stable microbiology.

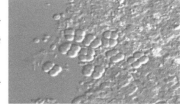

Figure: 7.10 tetrads cropped from 1000x DIC

- Removal of solids from primary clarifiers more frequently to reduce septicity/ lower the blanket levels of primary clarifiers.
    - o Processes that involve "co-thickening" of secondary waste activated sludge in the primary clarifiers are often extra suspectable to being sources of septicity as "hungry bugs" are being added to an area with high amounts of BOD and no supplied oxygen.
- Removal of a primary clarifier to reduce HRT values should organic acids be forming in the primary clarifiers.
- Removal of a selector zone should adequate conditions not be achieved (case specific).
- Increasing RAS rates to decrease the HRT of solids in final clarifier(s).
- Taking a final clarifier offline should it not be needed, and it is determined to be a source of septicity.
- Removal of excessive accumulated sludge accountable for benthic feedback of organic acids in lagoon and aerated stabilization processes.

Other Potential Precautions for Organic Acid Reduction Prior to Treatment

- Review of production/ reducing overall loading and/or loading surges to biological treatment process.
  - Note that EQ basins offer "buffering" capacity, however they can also be common sources of septicity/organic acid formation (case specific) if septic.
- Diversion of high strength (off spec) waste to a calamity tank ("spill tank") or other area, to be slowly bled in with the influent flow.
- Increasing the efficiency of primary treatment (such as DAF performance) to reduce loading on downstream processes (such as coupled anaerobic-aerobic processes).
- Biological reduction of organic acids from isolated "problem" areas prior to these streams entering the influent to the wastewater process.
  - i.e. Bioaugmentation (addition of commercial bacteria) and oxygen (free or combined as nitrate).
- Temporary or permanent elimination of septage or other high strength waste intake from outside sources.

Operational Control Strategies for Processes Treating Elevated Organic Acid Concentrated Wastewater (Richard, 2003)

- Implementation of step-feed.
- Putting additional basin(s) online to distribute loading more evenly.
- Modification from plug flow to complete mix process.
- Increasing the RAS rate (allowing higher MLSS and a lower F/M ratio at the front end of the aeration basin).
- Increasing internal recycle flows to anoxic selectors for BNR plants).

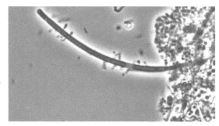

Figure: 7.11 Thiothrix cropped from 1000x phase contrast

- Increasing the MLSS concentration through the addition of other bacteria (i.e. fresh WAS from a nearby treatment plant).
  - See above for the risk involved with increasing MLSS concentrations. Often chlorination is needed in conjunction with increasing the MLSS concentration to "knock down" filaments while also helping to alleviate the root cause for their growth.
- Other (if possible)
  - Implementation/ Optimization of the Selector Zone

"Band-Aid" Options

- Settling Aids (Polymer, Coagulants etc.)
  - Consult the chemical vendor for jar testing/ assistance.
- Selective Chlorination
  - See the section later on this chapter about selective chlorination methods such as RAS chlorination to control filaments.

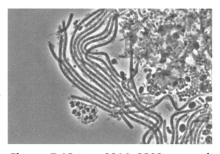

Figure: 7.12 type 0914_0803 cropped from 1000x phase contrast

7.1C Filamentous Bacteria Associated with Sulfide

Background

It is important to note that the majority filament types associated with sulfide are believed to be mixotrophs, meaning that they may utilize organic acids or sulfide for growth depending on what is available. In practice, we have found that precipitating or oxidizing sulfide may help reduce this cause. However if elevated organic acids still exist, bulking from these filaments remains likely.

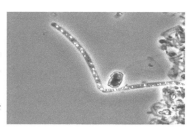

Figure: 7.13 Thiohtirx with sulfur granules phase

Filament Types Associated with Elevated Organic Acids and Sulfide

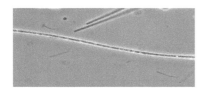

Figure: 7.14 Thiothrix with sulfur granules

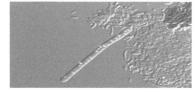

Figure: 7.15 type 021N with sulfur granules DIC 1000x cropped

Figure: 7.16 Beggiatoa DIC 1000x

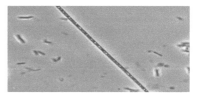

Figure: 7.17 type 0914 sulfur granules

- Beggiatoa
- Thiothrix
- Type 021N
- Type 0914/0803

Chemical Precipitation of Sulfide Mechanisms

- Iron salts (ferric, ferrous chloride)
- Potassium permanganate

Oxidation of Sulfide

- Hydrogen Peroxide
- Chlorine

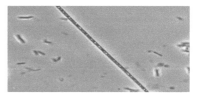

Figure: 7.18 iron sulfide 1000x phase contrast

Prevention of Sulfide Formation

- Aeration
- Adding Calcium Nitrate
- Anything else to raise ORP values closer to zero

ADDITIONALLY, NOTE THAT SULFIDE HAS THE POTENTIAL FOR BIOLOGICAL INHIBITION (TO BE DISCUSSED LATER WITHIN THIS CHAPTER).

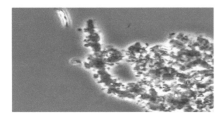

Figure: 7.19 type 0041_0675 cropped from 1000x phase

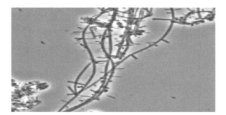

Figure: 7.20 type 1851 cropped from 1000x phase

Filamentous bacteria types 0041/0675 and 1851 are recognized as proliferating at elevated SRT values. Commonly elevated SRT values may coincide with prolonged periods (especially in extended aeration processes) in which food/substrate is limited to the bacteria on the "back end" of the aeration basin.

High SRT Filaments and Sludge Bulking

It is generally accepted that most genera that possess type 0041/0675 or type 1851 morphological traits are associated with the Chloroflexi or Patescibacteria phylum. Most Chloroflexi genera are fairly slow growing, and these filaments (in general) appear to have lower metabolic/maintenance needs allowing them to compete well when there are sufficient areas in which food/carbonaceous material is limited to the bacteria. Additionally, many Chloroflexi (such as Kouleothrix, which possess type 1851 morphology) may store sugars and other food under anaerobic conditions allowing this substrate to be utilized in times of lesser food availability (Dueholm et al., 2021; Speirs et al., 2019).

Filaments related to the Patescibacteria phylum (suspected to be mostly type 0041/0675) and certain families of the Chloroflexi phylum are believed to be more "cannibalistic" in nature preying on exocellular polysaccharide, or perhaps even other bacteria, as substrate. A theory related to excessive SRT values associated with pin floc is that these filament types degrade polysaccharide (which acts as "glue" to hold flocs together) making the flocs smaller. Eventually, when substrate is low enough that even the high SRT filaments cannot compete, pin flocs ("skeletons") are all that remain (M. Richard, Personal Communication). This process generally occurs over a considerable amount of time.

High SRT vs. Low F/M Ratio

While the above terms often occur together there are distinct differences of note. The F/M ratio is a particularly complex idea, as the amount of food available to microorganisms is constantly changing in conventional plug flow treatment processes. For example, the F/M ratio on the front end of the aeration basin may be extremely high, while the F/M in the latter part of the aeration basin may be extremely low. If the F/M ratio remains low enough for a sustained amount of time on the back end of the aeration basin, this may help filaments that compete well at low F/M ratio gain a competitive advantage due to their lower metabolic needs.

It is our opinion that it is best to judge F/M ratio not as a whole, but more as a curve representing available substrate starting high at the beginning of the processes and decreasing once available substrate becomes limited. Very often, the first 15-30 minutes (the "initial contact zone") of the aeration basin will be the most significant factor for which bacteria will compete for food in the process. At the initial contact zone of the aeration basin the majority of the organic acids are either taken up and oxidized or stored by bacteria for later usage later in the aeration basin. When organic acid concentrations are elevated, bacteria that have high kinetic growth rates and high storage availability may gain a competitive advantage.

An often unaccounted for aspect of F/M is the availability of the substrate. In instances where there is high septicity prior to biological treatment and BOD is fermented to the form of organic acids, these fractions are taken up or stored quickly, while particulate and more complex substrates need to be broken down by enzymes over a longer period of time before they can enter the cell membrane of the bacteria.

Oxygen uptake rate/ respirometry methods are commonly useful to judge the activity of the bacteria as the influent progresses down the aeration basin. If the majority of the substrate is taken up rapidly this has potential to leave a prolonged period of starvation for the bacteria allowing the conditions on the back end to enable a competitive advantage to bacteria with low metabolic needs. . These systems are often represented as "dual sludges" in which both the front end/ initial contact zone competition as well as the endogenous/starvation stage both become significant factors for the selection of bacteria present. In other systems, the F/M ratio and oxygen uptake rates may remain low throughout favoring only the growth of bacteria that compete well at low food availability.

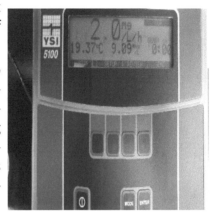
Figure: 7.22 OUR YSI, 2022

Sludge retention time is simply the amount of time that the average microbe stays in the system per calculation. It is possible to have a higher SRT value with or without low F/M present, particularly in industrial wastewater treatment systems (Smith, 2021) In addition to high SRT filaments, organic acid filaments such as type 0092, type 0961, type 0581 are often observed in systems with higher SRT values (M. Richard and R. Hennessy, observations).

Control Strategies for High SRT Filaments

Disclaimer

Before taking action to reduce high SRT filament types, a thorough microscopic evaluation is recommended with confirmation by a professional. It is common for high SRT filament types to be mis-diagnosed as they can often be mistaken for filament types such as Thiothrix or type 0914/0803. Filaments ranked common or less in abundance are generally not problematic and should be monitored but do not always create concern. As an example, there are several companies that conduct microscopy and also sell products, with a specific product recommended for each situation based on the microbiological findings regardless of if there is an actual problem. These companies often sell carbon sources (supplemental BOD) to plants that have any high SRT filaments, when the reality is that filaments exist in nearly all wastewater treatment plants and should only warrant operational intervention at predetermined key process indicators (such as SVI, 30-minute settling etc.).

Common Operational Control Strategies for High SRT Filaments

- Reducing the MLSS concentration.
- Reducing the SRT value (higher WAS rate).
- Taking basin(s) offline.
- Creating plug flow conditions (if possible).
- Carbon Supplementation
  - o Dog Food
    - For small municipal plants and small treatment plants such as plants designed for schools when school is out, dog food is often a good supplement.
      - Soft dog food tends to become soluble much more easily than dry dog food and dogs have a fairly similar diet to humans so bacteria in these processes are generally well acclimated.

Figure 7.22 molasses

- While not exact science, we have had success dosing 1 lb. of dog food to represent 1 lb. of BOD supplementation (M. Richard, personal communication).
  - o For larger applications dog food becomes less cost effective.

CAT FOOD, BIRD FOOD, AND OTHERS ARE GENERALLY NOT RECOMMENDED FOR DOMESTIC WASTEWATER CARBON SUPPLEMENTATION AS THESE ANIMALS HAVE SIGNIFICANTLY DIFFERENT DIETS THAN HUMANS.

- Other Carbon Sources
  - o Molasses
    - Molasses is generally cost effective and has a good BOD: N:P ratio.
  - o Addition of hauled-in industrial waste or septage.
    - Caution is needed to reduce the potential for slug loading issues, any potential inhibition/ toxicity, and additional potential issues such as fats, oils, and grease or nutrient ratios for certain industrial wastewaters.
  - o Glycol
    - Often a good source for industrial wastewater treatment plants that produce high sugar in waste as a byproduct (soda companies etc.)
      - Additional nutrient supplementation may be needed.
  - o Commercial Carbon Sources
    - There are many commercial carbon sources on the market that have been used with high success. Nutrient ratios of these sources may vary so if a significant amount of these products is added it is important to watch the BOD: N:P ratio of the influent.

MicroC®
Premium Carbon Sources.

MicroC 1000   MicroC 2000   MicroC 3000   MicroC 4000

Figure: 7.23 micro C carbon sources

"Band-Aid" Options

- Settling Aids (Polymer, Coagulants etc.)
  - o Consult chemical vendor for jar testing/ assistance.
- Selective Chlorination
  - o See Section later on this chapter about selective chlorination methods such as RAS chlorination to control filaments.

The Relationship Between MLSS Concentrations and Wasting Rates

While in general reducing the WAS rate increases the MLSS concentration, and vice versa the sludge yield/number of "bugs" produced is ultimately a main factor of the influent loading characteristics. In very lowly loaded municipal plants, it is fairly common to see wasting rates decrease or sometimes wasting stopped entirely, with no success in increasing the MLSS concentration. This phenomenon occurs because endogenous/ "starvation" conditions may exist allowing for cannibalistic activity (and corresponding decrease of volatile solids). Generally, if the SRT value is kept constant the MLSS concentration will drift to where it wants to be and in certain instances wasting may be needed to temporarily increase the F/M ratio to promote bacterial growth and raise the MLSS concentration. It is considered good operational practice to monitor SRT values and waste on a consistent basis regardless of the MLSS concentration value.

Figure: 7.24 pin floc 100x

Production Shutdowns

Based on Dr. Michael Richard's experience, if an industry is to experience a prolonged production shutdown, he recommends at least 25% of the daily loading supplemented if shutdown is one week or less. If shutdown periods are longer, a more representative percentage of the overall organic loading rate is needed to maintain the biomass characteristics.

7.1E Filaments Associated with Fats, Oils, and Grease (FOG)

Figure: 7.25 Actinomycetes_ Mycolata cropped from 1000x DIC

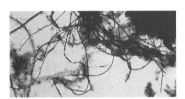

Figure: 7.26 Microthrix gram stain 1000x

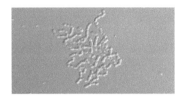

Figure: 7.27 type 1863 cropped DIC 1000x

Background

Actinomycetes-Mycolata filaments, Microthrix filaments, and type 1863 filament types are recognized to proliferate when fats, oils, and grease may be present at high concentrations. These filament types may either oxidize or store and then later oxidize lipids or commonly grow on long chain fatty acids produced from septic fats, oils, and grease (Dueholm et al., 2021). At lab scale, many of these filaments may utilize organic acids and glycol as substrate in addition to fats, oils, and grease however they are suspected to best compete for FOG in activated sludge processes.

There is high potential genetic diversity recognized within Actinomycetes-Mycolata filaments (possibly thousands of species), while type 1863 is most commonly associated with the Acinetobacter genus (which currently includes 90 specific species, some, but not all of which may possess a filamentous form with type 1863 morphology) (Dueholm et al., 2021; Doroghazi and Metcalf, 2013). Within the Ca Microthrix genus there are currently 6 recognized species and there are also closely related genera that may also possess Microthrix morphology (Dueholm et al., 2021).

Septicity Factor

It is commonly speculated that often the most significant variable in terms of FOG is the form and the availability of FOG to these filaments (M. Richard, theory). As an example, the same oil and grease concentrations observed in two separate treatment plants may be similar, however a treatment plant with high retention time in the collection system that promotes septicity may allow bacteria to ferment the FOG into unsaturated/ more readily accessible forms such as long chain fatty acids causing FOG filaments to proliferate at one treatment plant and not the other. This impact of septicity on FOG is commonly observed in treatment plants that never have a history of struggling with filaments such as Actinomycetes-Mycolata and Microthrix and then are upgraded with anaerobic/anoxic selector cells for enhanced biological nutrient removal. Many FOG classified filaments, such as filaments from the Microthrix genus, compete well in selector environments as they can store substrate under anaerobic conditions for later usage in addition to the FOG being exposed to septic conditions (Dueholm et al., 2021).

SRT Factor

SRT is defined as the amount of time an average microbe remains in the wastewater treatment plant. There are various calculations used with the general principle of lbs. of solids inventory/ lbs. of solids leaving the treatment plant per day to determine the SRT. Most conventional treatment plants operate in the range of 5-15 day SRT values, while extended aeration processes generally are operated at higher SRT values (such as 15-30 days) (Wisconsin Department of Natural Resources, 2016a).

Type 1863

It is suspected that filament type 1863 morphotypes commonly enter wastewater treatment processes through the influent and generally appear to correlate with recent FOG (Dueholm et al., 2021). Previous literature has suggested very low SRT values for these filaments to compete however we suspect that both (low SRT and entry through the influent) are likely growth causes. Increasing the SRT value if type 1863 filaments are present does not directly address the root cause (FOG) and often a shift to Actinomycetes-Mycolata or Microthrix filament types may be observed in these instances.

Microthrix

Historically Microthrix filament types appear to most commonly favor high SRT values, however experience has shown at certain plants that Microthrix may proliferate at lower SRT values than many textbooks say. In some instances, we suspect this may be the result of foam trapping dynamics (increasing the actual SRT) and in other instances it is likely that other species of Microthrix genus or genera similarly related may have slightly different growth rates. Many plants have had success with Microthrix by reducing the SRT value, however this tends to vary depending on each situation. For treatment plants that need to nitrify and have an ammonia limit, reducing the SRT (especially during the winter months) can often interfere with nitrification as many nitrifying bacteria have slow growth rates and need higher SRT values to compete in wastewater (Ripple, 2003).

Actinomycetes-Mycolata

In terms of the relationship between SRT and FOG filaments, Actinomycetes-Mycolata filaments appear to be the biggest "wildcard". We suspect that due to the high potential genetic diversity within the Actinomycetes-Mycolata morphotype that certain genera and species likely have higher growth rates than others. While some treatment plants report success with reducing SRT values to control Actinomycetes-Mycolata filament types, this may be ineffective at other treatment plants and also has the potential to interfere with nitrification.

Foam Trapping

All FOG classified filaments are also recognized to cause/contribute to foaming events in wastewater. When foam is trapped on the surface of the aeration basin this has potential to allow these filaments to gain a competitive advantage for available substrate. Many plants have reported success in controlling these filaments in certain instances by removing foam trapping features or removing foam from the surface of the aeration basin. Dr. David Jenkins believed that the likely predominant cause for many Actinomycetes-Mycolata issues may be related to foam trapping.

Figure: 7.28 Actinomycetes-Mycolata foam in oxidation ditch

Potential Operational Control Strategies for FOG Filaments

- Reduction of FOG at the source
  - o Grease trap ordinances.
  - o Required pretreatment for specific industries.
- Removal of FOG through primary treatment (DAF etc.)
- Reducing/Eliminating Potential Areas of Septicity
  - o If applicable- see section 7.1B.

- o Dr. Richard reports that some treatment plants have had success with abandoning anoxic/anaerobic selector cells to help control these filaments however other logistics such as total nitrogen limits, phosphorous limits, of costs associated with chemical removal of phosphorous all need to be considered in these instances.
- Reducing SRT values
  - o Occasionally successful with Microthrix and Actinomycetes-Mycolata filament types only.
- Eliminating Foam Trapping
  - o Foam trapping can be reduced through mechanical means or, in some instances, through allowing overflow rather than sub-surface flow transfer of wastewater as it moves through different basins in the treatment process.
- Settling Aids (Polymer, Coagulants etc.)
  - o Consult a chemical vendor for jar testing/ assistance.
- Selective Chlorination
  - o See section 7.2 about selective chlorination methods such as RAS chlorination to control filaments. Chlorination has also been applied selectively to foams such as Microthrix or Actinomycetes-Mycolata filament foams.
- De-Foaming/Anti-Foam Agents
  - o Long term usage of these products often has the potential to increase Microthrix and Actinomycetes-Mycolata abundance as the filaments in the foam may be "submerged" back into an environment that further promotes their growth.
    - Oil based defoamers may also serve as substrate for FOG filaments and it is generally considered good practice to avoid these in instances of FOG foaming/bulking filament related issues.
    - Contact a trusted chemical vendor for defoamer assistance.

DEFOAMER USAGE IS NOT IDEAL, HOWEVER IT BEATS THE ALTERNATIVE OF MICROTHRIX OR ACTINOMYCETES-MYCOLATA FOAMING EVENTS IN WHICH THE FOAM MAY "VOLCANO" OVER THE SURFACE OF THE AERATION BASIN ONTO THE GROUND OR AREA BELOW.

- Cationic polymer addition to RAS
  - o While not usually cost effective, some plants have had success with polymer addition to the RAS with the intention of "bringing the dispersed filaments back into the floc" and wasting them.
- Minimal to moderate engineering intervention
  - o Surface wasting.
  - o Selective wasting of RAS through separation by centrifugal methods (World Water Works, n.d.).

7.1F Low Nutrient Filamentous Bulking

Importance of Proper Diagnosis

All of the filamentous bacteria that may proliferate at low macronutrient availability have other potential growth causes, so it is essential to determine if nutrients are indeed limited or if filaments are growing for another reason. Per Dr. Michael Richard's request, we have removed low nitrogen availability as a growth cause for Thiothrix and type 021N filaments due to high amounts of mis-diagnosis events. Nutrient deficiency is extremely rare in municipal treatment processes and generally more likely to be encountered in industrial wastewater treatment processes.

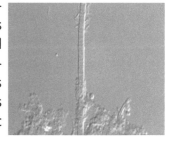

Figure: 7.29 type 021N cropped DIC 1000x

Diagnosing Nutrient Deficiency

When adequate nutrients are not available for the bacteria, cellular growth is shunted to the formation of exocellular polysaccharide rather than new "bug mass". A general recommendation is to ensure at least 1 mg/L residual of total inorganic nitrogen (nitrate + nitrite+ ammonia) and 1 mg/L of orthophosphate in the filtered mixed liquor/ biomass at the end of biological treatment prior to final liquid/solids separation (clarifier/DAF) at all times. Overgrowth of polysaccharide may cause/contribute to foaming and sludge bulking (Richard, 2003). Additionally, if macronutrients are scarce, certain filament types may gain a competitive advantage.

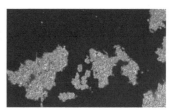

Figure 2.30 Elevated polysaccharide DIC 200x

Anthrone Testing

If polysaccharide as carbohydrates is >25% of dry weight of MLSS, low nutrient availability is suspected. Anthrone testing may be particularly useful in determining events of the previous sludge cycle as commonly nutrient deficiency occurs intermittently rather than constantly such as if nutrient supplementation is controlled manually and the BOD: N: P: ratio suddenly dramatically increases. We have also suspected low nutrient potential should toxicity/inhibition be present and suddenly the threshold of whatever is interfering with the enzymes of the bacteria reduces, causing rapid growth of bacteria that may exceed readily available nutrients.

Filament Types That May Potentially Proliferate at Low Nutrients

- Low Phosphorous
  - Haliscomenobacter
  - Nostocoida limicola III

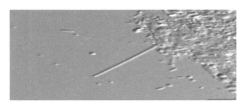

Figure: 7.31 Haliscomenobacter cropped from 1000x DIC

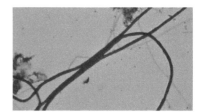

Figure: 7.32 Nostocoida limicola III Neisser

- Low Nitrogen
  - Rare/Not Common but Possible
    - Thiothrix
    - Type 021N

Figure: 7.33 Thiothrix rosette DIC 1000x cropped

Control of Filamentous Bulking Associated with Low Nutrients

- Ensure adequate supplementation of Nitrogen or Phosphorous.
- Wasting and reseeding, ensure proper nutrient availability.
- Settling Aids (Polymer, Coagulants etc.).
  - Consult a chemical vendor for jar testing/ assistance.
- Selective Chlorination:
  - See Section 7.2 about selective chlorination methods such as RAS chlorination to control filaments.

CAUTION: CHLORINATION FOR POLYSACCHARIDE BULKING IS NOT AN EFFECTIVE PRACTICE. THIS OFTEN RESULTS IN A "FOAMY MESS" AND ALSO INCREASES THE F/M RATIO FURTHER INCREASING THE NUTRIENT DEMAND AS WELL AS INCREASING POTENTIAL FOR POLYSACCHARIDE GROWTH RELATED TO ZOOGLOEA BACTERIA.

7.1G Low pH Issues

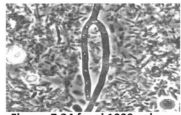

Figure: 7.34 fungi 1000x phase contrast

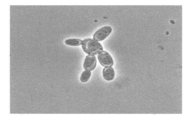

Figure: 7.35 yeast 1000x phase contrast

Biological wastewater treatment processes generally work best at pH ranges between 7-8.3. pH is a major factor on enzyme activity for bacteria and when the pH is outside of functional ranges a "changing of the guard" occurs in which other bacteria are then able to compete.

Fungi and Yeast

There are two major reasons why fungi and yeast may be observed in activated sludge processes.

- Low pH conditions somewhere within the system promoting their growth.
- Entering through the influent as a byproduct of production (i.e. food processing wastewater treatment plants).

It is common to see an occasional Fungi on a slide, however their abundance needs to be high enough (some-common) or it is likely simply incidental-insignificant growth.

Practical Applications

In our experience if the pH is outside of ideal ranges generally within approximately 24 hours a notable shift in the microbiology may occur. While bulking due to fungi is possible, it is often more common to see high dispersed growth, failure of nitrification, and lack of treatment and organisms such as fungi and yeast as the main indicator organism morphotypes.

Reasons for low pH

- If septicity occurs and acid forming bacteria surpass the alkalinity/buffering capacity of the wastewater the pH will drop. This situation also occurs in anaerobic processes in which the digester goes "sour", and the pH drops out of the range in which methanogens compete.
- A high amount of alkalinity is consumed through the nitrification process. Once alkalinity (buffering capacity) is depleted the pH may drop out of desired ranges.
- Some wastewater streams are naturally low in alkalinity and alkalinity must be supplemented to maintain desired pH values.

Chemistry for Increasing pH

- Calcium Carbonate
  - o Also good alkalinity source.
- Calcium Bicarbonate
  - o Also good alkalinity source.

- Magnesium Hydroxide
  - Also good alkalinity source.
- Calcium Hydroxide
- Sodium Hydroxide

Monovalent to Divalent Ratio Considerations

Calcium and magnesium are divalent cations and promote floc formation, while sodium is monovalent and at high enough concentrations may interfere with floc formation. Cost and other logistics come into play when choosing pH adjustment chemistry, however this is something to be aware of. In our experience, very high sodium is needed in most circumstances to significantly throw off the ratio.

7.2 Selective Chlorination for Filament Control

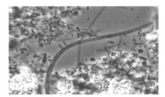
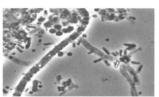
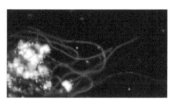

| Figure: 7.36 empty sheath dead filaments 1000x phase | Figure: 7.37 dead filaments 1000x phase | Figure: 7.38 predominantly dead filaments 1000x fluorescent cropped |

Background

In many instances, either filamentous bacteria may develop rapidly before operational changes are implemented to discourage their growth or chronic conditions may be present that continually allow for the selection of filamentous bacteria. While permanent fixes are always preferred, cost-benefit analysis of the options should be determined prior to selecting a control strategy. The first and most essential step in this process is an accurate microscopy assessment with proper diagnosis of the root cause of filament growth.

In many situations, such as trying to reduce septicity in collection systems or other areas, the cost associated with reducing filament growth may not be economically viable. In many instances, the most practical option is to let filaments grow and selectively kill them through RAS chlorination. Prior to the decision to chlorinate, not only is proper diagnosis through microscopy needed, but also evaluation of "band-aid options" such as chlorination vs. settling aids.

Filaments are highly efficient at oxidizing BOD and in overloaded treatment plants it is important to consider that killing filaments may significantly increase the F/M ratio in the initial contact zone of the aeration basin, which may have undesired effects of creating high dispersed bacteria growth or proliferation of zoogloea-type bacteria. It is also useful to take the floc structure into consideration. For example, strong flocs with filaments bridging the flocs are better candidates for RAS chlorination than open/diffuse flocs in which filaments are predominantly located in the flocs (in these instances "collateral damage" is likely with chlorination). Choosing between settling aids and RAS chlorination is a case-by-case situation and ideally it is good to consult with a professional with expertise in this area prior to making any decisions. In general, the larger the treatment plant and higher the daily average flow rate, the less economical settling aids become. Ultimately, factors such as urgency, cost dynamics, and compliance are key factors for these decisions.

7.2A Dosing Criteria for RAS Chlorination

RAS chlorination dosage is generally targeted based on lbs. of active chlorine in proportion to lbs. of volatile suspended solids in the MLSS. RAS chlorination should be constant, with chlorine injected into a place with good mixing (such as tapping into RAS lines). Chlorination in poor mixing areas, such as RAS wet wells, can lead to an uneven distribution of chlorine, effectively overdosing certain areas and underdosing others. Chlorine should come into contact with each microbe a minimum of 2x per day for optimal exposure (Jenkins et al., 2004). In most conventional treatment systems dosing chlorine to only the RAS line meets these criteria. However in larger treatment plants with high HRT, such as extended aeration processes, an additional chlorination point may be needed to meet the desired frequency (such as a side-stream loop from the aeration basin or dosage to the center well of the clarifier in addition to the RAS line.) Ideally, chlorine is introduced at a time when there are low competing reactions and biological treatment is completed.

Common RAS Chlorine Dosage Rates

(Jenkins et al., 2004)

- 2-3 lbs. chlorine per 1000 lbs. MLSS
  - Considered "low"/ often used as a "maintenance dose"
- 5-6 lbs. chlorine per 1000 lbs. MLSS
  - Common dose for selectively killing filaments over several days with minimum impact to effluent quality.
- >6 lbs. chlorine per 1000 lbs. MLSS
  - These dosage rates are considered high in general, however the amount of chlorine needed to selectively kill filaments may vary considerably depending on the chlorine demand and competing reactions.

FOR THESE CALCULATIONS, POUNDS OF ACTIVE CHLORINE ARE USED. FOR EXAMPLE, IF USING SODIUM HYPOCHLORITE AT 12.5% ACTIVE CHLORINE THIS MUST BE ACCOUNTED FOR IN THE CALCULATION.

Caution

Chlorination of the RAS line should ideally be done by experienced operators. When in doubt, chlorine rates may always be increased, however severe unintended consequences (floc break up, high dispersed growth, potential loss of effluent quality) may occur if chlorine is significantly overdosed.

Monitoring RAS Chlorination

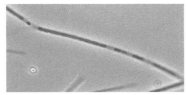

Figure: 7.40 Sphaerotilus with damaged cells

Figure: 7.41 Chlorine damage Haliscomenobacter filaments

When chlorination of the RAS is implemented to control filament growth, daily microscopic evaluation at high power (1000x oil immersion phase contrast) is recommended to help control the chlorine dosage. If after a day there is no notable death or damage to filaments, the chlorine dosage may not be high enough to meet the demand and may be cautiously increased. At the point in which 50-60% of filaments contain damaged cells and/or empty sheaths it is recommended to significantly reduce or stop chlorination to prevent overdose.

NOTE THAT RAS CHLORINATION ONLY SELECTIVELY KILLS FILAMENTS ONCE THEY HAVE GROWN AND OFTEN WHEN CHLORINATION IS STOPPED FILAMENTS MAY GROW BACK RAPIDLY IF CONDITIONS EXIST TO PROLIFERATE THEIR GROWTH.

Abnormal Chlorination Situations

Certain processes, such as SBRs (sequencing batch reactors) do not have a RAS line in which chlorination can be added. In these situations, a higher risk chlorination approach termed by Dr. Richard as the "hypo bomb" may be implemented. In these instances, a large dose of chlorine is added approximately 30 minutes prior the final settling cycle, after the majority of BOD removal/ competing reactions have been reduced. There is a calculation we have had success with for determining the amount of chlorine to be used, however due to the high risk associated with overdosing we feel that these decisions should be discussed with trained professionals prior to being used in practice.

7.3 "Sludge Juggling" and High Flow Events

There are certain instances in which small modifications may be implemented to help reduce the solids loading rate imposed on the final clarifiers in conditions or poor settling or elevated hydraulic flow rates. For example, should a treatment plant have an additional aeration basin that may be put in service, this will store more solids within the system effectively lowering the MLSS concentration and the ensuing solids loading rates to the final clarifier(s) are decreased. Some treatment plants have had success through these means in which eventually the microbiology returns to desired conditions and the basin may then be taken offline again (Richard, 2003).

Some treatment plants have the ability to shift to contact stabilization mode, in which the RAS is fed to the front end of the aeration basin and the influent is fed downstream after aeration/stabilization of the RAS. Contact stabilization configuration allows a shift to higher solids concentrations at the front end of the system with the influent diluting the solids concentration and the corresponding solids loading rate imposed on the final clarifier(s).

Many municipal plants struggle with major hydraulic surges posed by the inflow and infiltration during weather events such as heavy rain falls or snow melt. During these events in some instances the hydraulic flow rates have the potential to cause clarifier failure in which the solids cannot be returned or wasted faster than they accumulate and are eventually lost over the clarifier weirs. Flexibility for "bottling the solids" is highly dependent on the final effluent treatment limits and the degree to which inflow and infiltration rates dilute the influent wastewater concentrations (BOD, TSS, etc.) Some treatment plants report success with temporary solids redistribution through methods such as turning off the mixing in selector zones, bypassing selector zones and storing thickened RAS in them, or in extreme cases, temporarily turning off aeration to allow the mixed liquor to settle out and the high flows to pass through to the clarifier without the corresponding solids loading rates. In practical experience, the latter has been used successfully in some instances for periods of several hours to allow the RAS to remain running and decrease the sludge blankets to manageable levels where aeration may then be restored. Note that "high flow procedures" are specific to each plant's specific circumstances and all temporary changes during these events should be documented.

7.4 Common Engineering Modifications for Filamentous Bulking Control

7.4A Tertiary DAF

Occasionally portable tertiary DAF (Dissolved Air Floatation) units may be rented to capture suspended solids that aren't removed by the clarifier prior to the final effluent. Note that due to potential of changing solids rate to tertiary DAF units as well as changes to chemistry demand, vigilance may be needed to successfully optimize DAF chemistry.

In certain industrial processes, final clarifiers have been permanently replaced by DAF units. In these situations, sludge quality is not as important as highly filamentous sludges tend to float easily with the DAF effectively operating as a clarifier in which sludge is thickened and then returned (RAS) or wasted (WAS).

7.4B Primary DAF

DAF units accompanied by the proper chemistry are efficient for removing fats, oils, and grease, and in certain mainly industrial processes, have been implemented prior to activated sludge processes. A well-functioning primary DAF system will remove BOD associated with fats, oils, and grease and particulate solids; however soluble BOD/organic acids are not removed in these processes.

7.4C Moving Bed Bio Reactor (MBBR)

In MBBR processes, floating media are added to the aeration basin or a section of the aeration basin allowing for higher viable bacteria available for treatment without the corresponding increased solids loading rates on the final clarifier(s) (Frankel, 2019). Generally, MBBR areas are designated to lower the F/M ratio in the "initial contact zone" of the aeration basin with the intention of discouraging filamentous bacteria that have high kinetic growth rates and high PHB storage capacity.

7.4D Step Feed

Step feed involves introducing the influent to the aeration basin at various locations rather than having 100% of the influent flow mixed with the RAS at the initial contact zone. Step feeding has often been implemented successfully to control organic acid filaments or low DO filaments; however, it is not recommended for controlling high SRT filament types.

Step feed modification should be done with the help of a trusted engineering professional and step feed locations can be determined through oxygen uptake studies (for example once the OUR rate decreases this area could then again be fed with influent). Commonly in 2-part step feed processes, approximately 70% of the influent is fed to the front-end initial contact zone of the aeration basin and the remaining 30% is fed approximately 1/3 of the way down the aeration basin. Multiple step-feed configurations have been successfully implemented at various plants with up to 5 different step feed locations by engineers such as Rick Marshall of METC.

Often, step feeding has been tried using methods such as hoses and trash pumps and, should it be successful, a more permanent solution may be implemented. In many situations, automation of desired flow rates for the step feeds is not economically practical and flow is measured less scientifically (such as with a stopwatch and 5-gallon bucket, or # of turns a valve is open).

IN STEP FEED SITUATIONS, IT IS ESSENTIAL THAT ENOUGH HRT REMAINS IN THE BASIN FOR PROCESSES SUCH AS BOD REMOVAL AND NITRIFICATION, SHOULD NITRIFICATION BE NEEDED.

7.4E Implementation of Selector Cells

Selector cells have been proven effective in controlling organic acid and low DO filamentous bulking provided they are designed and operated efficiently. Both an underloaded and an overloaded selector cell have the potential to cause more harm than good if they are not operated within the "sweet spot" (Gray et al., 2010). The methodology involved with selector cells implies utilizing the advantage that certain floc forming bacteria have over many filaments, such as uptake and storage of VFAs under anaerobic or anoxic conditions for later usage in the aeration basin.

In nitrifying processes, the nitrate returned through the RAS or mixed liquor internal recycling may serve as an oxygen acceptor for denitrification, effectively promoting BOD removal as well as new cellular growth and restoring alkalinity, lessening the organic acid concentrations of the selector effluent as it reaches the initial contact zone of the aeration basin. If ORP values can be reached in which storage by other bacteria (such as PAOs) is accomplished this also has the ability to further decrease organic acid loading rates in the initial contact zone of the aeration basin. Generally, soluble BOD removal of 60% or higher is desired in selector cells (Jenkins et al., 2004). In overloaded selector cells, organic acids may pass through the selector into the initial contact zone and in underloaded cells, formation of organic acids without storage by bacteria may occur.

Aerobic selector cells exist but have become less common. For these processes to work it is essential that the necessary oxygen is supplied, or the cell may become septic, or a growth area for low DO filamentous bacteria.

7.4F Roughing Filter

Using a roughing filter is a process that behaves similarly to MBBR, however the biomass grows on a fixed film media rather than suspended media. The objective of a roughing filter is to oxidize organic acids prior to entering the initial contact zone of the selector (Nkwonta and Ochieng, 2009). Coupled fixed film-suspended growth and activated sludge processes have commonly been implemented to upgrade the initial fixed-film-only processes to increase organic loading rates or meet more stringent effluent requirements. While the science is unclear, our experience has shown that fixed film systems appear to have less common bulking events associated with FOG filaments. If a roughing filter is overloaded, septicity and the formation of further organic acids may occur within the media, potentially doing more harm than good (similarly to an overloaded selector cell). Roughing filters are not desired for control of high SRT filaments as they reduce organic loading rates to the aeration basin.

7.4G Membrane Bioreactor (MBR)

MBR processes have become more common as they generally produce high quality effluent, have a small footprint, and permeability takes priority over settleability. In MBR systems, the clarifier is replaced by a membrane filter for final liquid-solids separation. Usually, filamentous sludges permeate well and do not cause issues with membrane performance. MBR systems often encounter trouble when the membranes foul rapidly, requiring more frequent backwashing/CIP processes (Iorhemen et al., 2016). For the MBR process to be successful, the permeate needs to be able to keep up to the rate of the hydraulic loading imposed on the aeration basin. Dispersed single cell bacteria, dispersed "fines"/dead cellular material, and polysaccharide are common foulants in MBR systems. While initially thought to reduce the need for microscopy evaluations, experience has shown that microscopic evaluation with a focus on reducing fouling potential (and less emphasis on filament control) remains a highly useful tool when implied accurately in the desired circumstances.

7.4H Tertiary Filtration

Tertiary filtration involves the addition of a filter after the secondary clarifier to further reduce suspended solids carryover into the effluent. Tertiary filtration processes are becoming increasingly common as phosphorous limits become increasingly stringent (2-3% of MLSS by weight is typically composed of phosphorous with higher amounts in plants where enhanced biological phosphorous removal is occurring) (Evoqua Water Technologies, 2021).

As the filter begins to foul, head loss occurs, eventually leading to backwashing of the filter. In bulking events, if the solids loading rate to the tertiary filter surpasses the backwashing/cleaning capability of the filter, the process will fail.

7.4I Calamity Ponds

In some instances (particularly in industrial processes) wastewater that is out of compliance for discharge may be re-directed to a pond or a series of ponds, where it can then be retreated and bled back in slowly with the influent or effluent when the biological treatment plant recovers. These ponds provide short term solutions, or in some instances even moderately longer periods of time, for the treatment plant to recover.

Calamity ponds are often limited by hydraulic holding capacity and depending on them can create additional issues such as odor or solids accumulation/ benthic feedback and eventual dredging. It is considered good operational practice to identify the root cause of process control failure immediately if effluent is not suitable for discharge and being diverted to calamity ponds.

7.4J Equalization (EQ) Basins

If loading rates to a treatment plant are highly variable, often the F/M ratio may be controlled (to various extents) through controlling the flow from an EQ basin to the downstream biological treatment process. EQ basins may be beneficial for filament control as slug loading may encourage the proliferation of filaments with high kinetic growth rates and high PHB storage capabilities as well as keep loading consistent, especially in instances in which production is only 5 days out of the week, allowing the loading rate to be spread over the course of the entire week.

If EQ basins become septic, they have the potential to do more harm than good as they are often a source of organic acid formation.

In some processes that may or may not include an EQ basin, another basin or area may exist as a calamity tank (or "spill tank") in which known high-strength waste or other "off spec" wastewater can either be added back to the influent or EQ basin or hauled to a different facility for treatment.

7.4K Anaerobic Pretreatment

In some processes, upstream anaerobic pretreatment prior to secondary/biological treatment are implemented to reduce organic acid loading rates to the secondary treatment process. In anaerobic pretreatment processes, ideally high percentages of organic acids/VFAs are converted to methane gas and other gaseous byproducts. Methane may either be flared off or used to generate power, such as electricity that may offset costs in other areas such as aeration, boiler operation, or production.

Costs associated with installing anaerobic pretreatment are high and if anaerobic reactors are overloaded, they may also create periods of elevated organic acid loading to downstream biological processes. In food-processing wastewater, it is common for grease caps to develop in anaerobic systems and the grease may solubilize (especially at higher temperatures) resulting in occasional slug loading to the downstream process. Ideally, factors such as mixing and consistent solids removal from anaerobic processes are in place to mitigate these risks.

7.4L Upgrading Treatment Capacity

These options include processes such as adding aeration basins, clarifiers, or a combination of one or more of the methods described above. Note that other methods exist, however the focus of this book is not on engineering, but rather understanding wastewater microbiology.

Chapter 8:

Other Troubleshooting Tips and Strategies

8.1 "Slime Bulking"

8.2 Pin Floc

8.3 Denitrification

8.4 Dispersed Growth

8.5 Foaming in Aerobic Biological Processes

8.6 Stress, Inhibition, and Toxicity

Introduction

While the previous chapter discussed operational control methods for bulking associated with filamentous bacteria, this chapter will address troubleshooting tips and strategies for other common problems as introduced in Chapter 2.

8.1 "Slime Bulking"

Figure: 8.1 zoogloea cropped from 1000x DIC

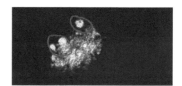

Figure: 8.2 zoogloea polysaccharide 200x DIC

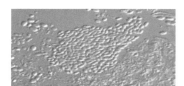

Figure: 8.3 zoogloea cropped from 1000x DIC

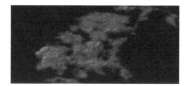

Figure: 8.4 elevated polysaccharide zoogloea 400x DIC

Background

As discussed in Chapter 2, excessive polysaccharide commonly contributes to weak/viscous floc structure and in severe instances, can cause true "slime bulking" in which polysaccharide acts similarly to filamentous bacteria bridging flocs together and increasing the SVI value. Excessive polysaccharide is most often attributed to the proliferation of zoogloea type bacteria or low availability of nutrients (Jenkins et al., 2004). It is rare for nutrients to be limited in domestic municipal wastewater treatment processes.

8.1A Zoogloea Troubleshooting Tips and Strategies

Zoogloea bacteria types (most commonly associated with the Zoogloea and Thauera genera) are recognized to proliferate at elevated organic acid concentrations and when there is a high F/M ratio in the initial contact zone of the aeration basin (Hennessy, 2020).

Operational Considerations for Zoogloea Bulking

(Richard, 2003)

- Increase the MLSS concentration to lower the F/M ratio in the initial contact zone.
- Increase of the SRT/ reduce the WAS rate.
- Step feed the influent throughout the basin.
- Prevent organic acid formation (see Chapter 8, organic acid filaments).
- Reduce organic acids at the source by:
  - o Reducing the overall loading rates.
  - o Bioaugmentation and adding oxygen sources, targeting known loading streams high in VFAs to reduce them prior to biological treatment.
  - o Others
    - See engineering options in previous chapter for organic acid control.
- Putting an additional aeration basin online, if possible, to spread out the organic loading more evenly.

- If possible, avoiding plug flow conditions/ switching to a complete mix configuration.
- Implementation or optimization of selector cells.
- Increasing the RAS rate:
  o To an extent, it dilutes incoming organic acid concentrations.
  o Fewer solids may be held in the clarifier, lowering the F/M ratio in the initial contact zone of the aeration basin.
- Any potential precautions to avoid slug loading.
  o EQ tanks.
  o Spill tanks/ calamity ponds etc.
- Adding Coagulant and other settling aids.
  o Contact a reputable chemical vendor.

DO NOT CHLORINATE THE RAS IF BULKING IS ATTRIBUTED TO ZOOGLOEA BACTERIA AS THIS OFTEN LEADS TO MAJOR FOAMING AND ALSO FURTHER ENCOURAGES ZOOGLOEA GROWTH AND DISPERSED GROWTH AS THE F/M RATIO IS INCREASED THROUGH CHLORINATION REDUCING THE VIABILITY OF THE MLSS (RICHARD, 2003).

8.1B Polysaccharide Bulking Due to Nutrient Deficiency

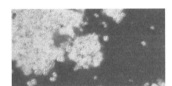

Figure: 8.5 elevated polysaccharide low nutrients

Figure: 8.6 viscous flocs low nutrients 100x phase

Diagnosing Nutrient Deficiency

When adequate nutrients are not available for the bacteria, cellular growth is shunted to the formation of exocellular polysaccharide rather than new bug mass. A general recommendation is to ensure at least 1 mg/L residual of total inorganic nitrogen (nitrate + nitrite+ ammonia) and 1 mg/L of orthophosphate in the filtered mixed liquor/ biomass at the end of biological treatment prior to final liquid/solids separation (clarifier/DAF) at all times (Richard, 2003). Overgrowth of polysaccharide may cause/contribute to foaming and sludge bulking. Additionally, if macro nutrients are scarce, certain filament types may gain a competitive advantage.

IT IS GOOD PRACTICE TO TEST RESIDUAL NUTRIENTS OF THE FILTERED MIXED LIQUOR/BIOMASS PRIOR TO THE FINAL CLARIFIER AS ORTHOPHOSPHATE AND AMMONIA MAY BE RE-RELEASED IN THE CLARIFIER SHOULD SEPTICITY OCCUR IN THE SLUDGE BLANKET.

Anthrone Testing

If polysaccharide as carbohydrates is >25% of the dry weight of the MLSS, low nutrient availability is suspected. Anthrone testing may be particularly useful in determining events of the previous sludge cycle, as commonly nutrient deficiency occurs intermittently rather than constantly (Richard, 2003). One such example is if nutrient supplementation is controlled manually and the BOD: N: P: ratio suddenly dramatically increases. We have also suspected low nutrient potential should toxicity/inhibition be present and suddenly the threshold of whatever is interfering with the enzymes of the bacteria reduces causing rapid growth of bacteria that may exceed readily available nutrients (Richard, 2003).

Macronutrients

- Nitrogen
- Phosphorus

Practical Application

In our experience, macronutrient deficiency is almost always the cause of any nutrient deficiency. Phosphorous is part of the Krebs cycle and without phosphorous, bacterial cell growth is immediately shunted to exocellular polysaccharide production (Science Direct, n.d.). Nitrogen availability tends to be a little more forgiving as bacteria have internally stored protein that can be utilized, however while cost associated with nutrient supplementation is always a factor, it is considered good operational practice to always be on the safe side.

Micronutrients

(Jenkins et al., 2004)

- Potassium
- Calcium
- Magnesium
- Sulfur
- Sodium
- Chloride
- Iron
- Zinc
- Manganese
- Copper
- Molybdenum
- Cobalt

Practical Application

In Dr. Richard's decorated career of over 40 years, he has encountered only one instance in which micronutrient deficiency was diagnosed in an aerobic biological wastewater treatment process. This incident involved an industry that made a shift from using city water to distilled water in the production process. The industry shifted back to city water and the treatment plant returned to normal. This is not to say that micronutrient deficiency does not exist, however it may be beneficial to start with macronutrients, the influent BOD:N:P ratio, and residual orthophosphate and total inorganic nitrogen concentrations in the filtered biomass at the end of treatment.

From a treatment standpoint, micronutrient dosing does not pose any threats, however due to the high number of variables present in any wastewater process it is very difficult to conduct true case studies. Micronutrients are commonly applied to anaerobic processes in industrial wastewater treatment and there is a fair amount of literature stating potential positive benefits (Myszorgrai et al., 2018).

Anthrone Testing as a Tool for Nutrient Dosing Control

Many plants use the percentage of polysaccharide (as carbohydrate) per dry weight of the biomass as a monitoring tool for nutrient supplementation rates. For example, nutrient deficiency is officially suspected at above 25% polysaccharide per dry weight MLSS. If a plant is supplementing nutrients and the percentage of polysaccharide observed in the Anthrone test is low (i.e. 10%), this suggests that nutrient addition may potentially be cautiously scaled back. If the percentage of polysaccharide increases close to 20%, this may be a good indicator that higher nutrient feed may be needed to avoid upcoming potential issues with limited nutrients.

Factors for Nutrient Demand

The classic 100:5:1 BOD:N:P ratio minimum is generally considered a conservative "starting point" (Jenkins et al., 2004). At higher temperatures in the aeration basin there is a higher metabolic rate for the bacteria with potential for endogenous conditions to occur. When bacteria die due to starvation/endogeny, cell lysis occurs which re-releases nutrients that are stored which may then be internally recycled by other bacteria. This process may effectively lower the actual nutrient demand. Also, nutrient demand is higher at cold temperatures as bacteria functions tend to shift more toward growth and less to cell maintenance, endogeny, and cell lysis. Therefore, it is common for real-time nutrient demand for similar loading rates to be higher at colder temperatures than warmer temperatures. Lastly, SRT values may also play a role in nutrient demand. Lower SRT values promote more growth and a higher nutrient demand, while higher SRT values tend to encourage endogenous activity in which nutrients may be internally recycled and reused.

Macronutrient Supplements

The most important factor for macronutrient supplements is that the nutrients need to be in a readily accessible form for the bacteria when BOD oxidation occurs (Jenkins et al., 2004). Phosphorous is readily available to bacteria in the form of orthophosphate and nitrogen is readily available in the form of ammonia or nitrate. Some common nitrogen supplements such as urea need to undergo hydrolysis for ammonia to be formed and readily available. While this reaction typically happens rapidly and is typically successful, there are extreme cases in which urea may not produce its ammonia byproduct in time due to high amounts of readily available carbonaceous material. In these instances, a more readily available form of ammonia (such as aqua ammonia) may be needed.

Consequences of Overdosing Nutrients

Phosphorous

Excess phosphorous does not have a negative impact on the microbiology and simply passes through to the effluent. The larger implications of overdosing phosphorous are related to potential effluent total phosphorous limits, the cost of the phosphorous supplement, and any potential chemical removal of phosphorous needed to precipitate additionally dosed phosphorous to keep effluent limits within permitted levels.

Nitrogen

Overdosing nitrogen can become more complicated and has a higher potential risk to the microbiology. For example, if nitrogen is overdosed and conditions allow, nitrification may occur which creates a substantial oxygen and alkalinity demand. Also, when nitrate is formed through the process of nitrification, this may increase the potential for denitrification related problems, such as floating sludge in the final clarifier(s) (Richard, 2003).

When supplementing nitrogen, it is especially important to look at nitrite and nitrate residuals in addition to ammonia. We have commonly seen plants overdosing nitrogen supplements because they are targeting a desired ammonia concentration residual. Should nitrification or even partial nitrification (oxidization to nitrite) occur, this indicates excess available nitrogen. Lastly, we have found circumstances where monitoring read % of nitrifying bacteria genera through DNA analysis may also help determine if a nitrifying population is forming. As an example, in a particular industrial plant if Nitrospira reads become >1% supplemental nitrogen is reduced to limit nitrification.

Plants with Highly Variable BOD:N Ratio

Occasionally in certain instances, operational staff must decide whether to dose nitrogen closely and limit nitrification, or whether to allow for a population of nitrifying bacteria to grow. For example, if a plant is 100% reliant on nitrogen removal through nutrient uptake and the BOD significantly drops but the available nitrogen remains the same, it is possible for very high residual ammonia concentrations to suddenly be present. If nitrifying bacteria are present, this may allow for some forgiveness in these circumstances. In other instances, we have had success storing and adding high strength waste with low nitrogen content to get the BOD: N ratio back into balance reducing residual ammonia. In instances in which high strength waste with high BOD:N ratio is not available commercial supplemental BOD sources (generally high in carbon and low in macronutrients) have been useful to quickly adjust this nutrient balance and reduce effluent ammonia through cellular assimilation.

8.2 Pin Floc

Background

Pin flocs are flocs <50 μm in dimension by definition (Jenkins et al., 2004). Pin floc is associated with chronic stress (many potential causes) or low F/M ratio on the back end of the aeration basin/ starvation/ endogeny (Jenkins et al., 2004). When pin flocs proliferate either a rapidly settling sludge (low SVI) value may occur, in which there is little forgiveness for any dispersed growth (often producing a turbid supernatant), or the settling may become poor as the small negatively charged floc particles repel against each other (think "pinball") without the gravitational impact of strong flocs to overcome this force.

Figure: 8.7 low viabilitly 400x

Importance of Proper Diagnosis and Routine Microscopy

Any time the SVI value drifts out of pre-defined "ideal" values, a thorough microscopic evaluation is recommended immediately to determine the cause of the change. Elevated SVI due to pin floc/poor floc structure is often not properly diagnosed and we have encountered several plants that have assumed the SVI increase is related to filaments, in which RAS chlorination is implemented and the problems become worsened.

Common Pin Floc Causes
- Old sludge/a high SRT/ low F/M ratio on the back end of the system/ endogeny/ starvation.
- Stress or chronic stress from:
  - Very low dissolved oxygen concentrations
  - Limited alkalinity/ pH swings
  - Presence of inhibitory compounds
  - Others (various)
- Combination of one or more of the above

8.2A Diagnosing the Cause of Pin Floc

Figure: 8.8 pin floc 200x DIC

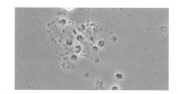

Figure: 8.9 dead cellular material 1000x phase

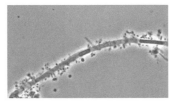

Figure: 8.10 dead filament 1000x phase

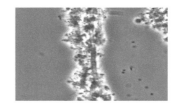

Figure 8.11 type 0041_0675 1000x phase

From a microscopy perspective, diagnosing pin floc is fairly straightforward. Often, the biggest challenge lies in that pin floc can be caused by old/over-oxidized sludge or as a result of chronic stress within the system. This is a prime example of why it is essential to look at the surrounding microbiology for clues as to what may be causing the pin floc.

Example #1

Flagellates are high in abundance, high dispersed single cell bacteria are present, and Sphaerotilus and type 1701 filaments are growing dispersed in solution. These findings suggest it is likely that there was a pre-existing condition of a chronic stress (or even possibly a very low F/M) and now either the stress has reduced below the inhibition threshold, or the organic loading rate has greatly increased.

Example #1 Recommendations

In an instance such as this, decreasing the WAS rate is generally recommended to allow the F/M ratio to become lower on the initial contact zone of the aeration basin in attempts to reduce the oxygen uptake rate and bacterial growth rates. Additionally, the low DO filaments suggest that (if possible) increasing the available DO or DO setpoint may be warranted.

Example #2

Pin flocs are high in abundance, occasional dispersed "fines'/dead cellular material are present, mode-rate amounts of filament type 1851 and type 0041/0675 are present in addition to pin floc. Rotifers are predominant along with crustaceans and occasional tardigrades (water bear). The SVI has decreased to 40 mL/g. and the mixed liquor settles rapidly.

Example #2 Recommendations

These findings suggest an old/over-oxidized sludge and that the F/M ratio may be too low. A common recommendation would be increasing the WAS rate and lowering the SRT value.

Other Examples and Putting the "Big Picture" Together

Often, diagnosing the root cause of pin floc may be challenging, especially if there are low/insignificant levels of other indicator microorganism types present within the sample to help diagnose the cause. In these instances, analytical data and a greater understanding of the scenarios may be useful to help diagnose what is occurring. For example, if the municipal treatment plant is in a town with high tourism and the tourism season has ended along with significantly reduced flows and loading/ pin floc is most likely to be attributed to old sludge conditions.

NOTE THAT REGARDLESS OF THE MICROSCOPIC EVALUATION SAMPLE FINDINGS, AN UNDERSTANDING OF THE PLANT, ANY OUTLYING CIRCUMSTANCES, AND THE DESIRED TREATMENT GOALS ARE NECESSARY BEFORE CONSIDERING ANY POTENTIAL OPERATIONAL CHANGES OR OFFERING ANY OPERATIONAL ADVICE.

DNA Applications for Pin Floc Diagnosis

Occasionally, other than pin floc, there may be limited clues in the surrounding microbiology to help assess the potential cause of pin floc. In our experience, community analysis (16SrRNA) may be beneficial in these instances to help identify the genetic properties of the bacteria that are responsible for the pin floc. For example, if the findings show a high percentage of bacteria that ferment organic material to propionic acid, it may be expected that septicity/fermentation to propionic acid (an odd-numbered carbon organic acid) may be related to the pin floc and reducing septicity may need to be addressed to encourage floc forming bacteria. If high Patescibacteria phylum reads (suspected polysaccharide degraders) are present, then pin floc may be attributed to proliferation of bacteria that degrade polysaccharide when other carbon sources are scarce.

Figure: 8.12 DNA testing

8.3 Denitrification

Figure: 8.13 floating sludge in clarifier

Figure: 8.14 floating sludge in clarifier

Figure: 8.15 denitrification settlometer

Denitrification Defined

Denitrification is the process simply defined as a biochemical reaction in which nitrate is converted to nitrogen gas through oxidation of a carbon source. For denitrification to occur, the following three variables are needed (Wisconsin Department of Natural Resources, 2018):

1. Anoxic conditions. (No free dissolved oxygen present).

2. The presence of nitrate.

3. A carbon source (soluble carbonaceous material or substrate that is internally stored by the bacteria) (Wisconsin Department of Natural Resources, 2018).

   - See the denitrification section in Chapter 2 for more details on the impacts on treatment performance and settling.

8.3A Denitrification and Oxygen Uptake Rate

Often denitrification is caused by either soluble carbonaceous material or internally stored substrate (PHB granules within filaments/bacteria) creating an increased oxygen uptake rate as the mixed liquor enters the final clarifier(s).

8.3B Common Control Strategies for Denitrification Issues

(Richard, 2003)

   - Increase the MLSS concentration to create a more stable and oxidized mixed liquor (decrease of oxygen uptake rate) prior to the clarifier.

   - Increase the RAS rate to reduce the HRT of sludge in the clarifier reducing the risk of free dissolved oxygen becoming depleted.

- Removal of a final clarifier to reduce HRT values.
- Increase DO prior to the final clarifier to allow a greater DO residual for usage of bacteria in the clarifier before nitrate would be utilized.
- Improve sludge quality.
    o Often, sludges that are highly filamentous are more efficient at trapping nitrogen gas and more prone to floating. Finding the root causes of filaments and/or selectively chlorinating (when applicable) to improve sludge quality offers more "lanes" for the nitrogen gas to escape to the atmosphere rather than become entrapped within the floc.
- Improve mixing prior to the final clarifier.
    o In an instance in which denitrification was interfering with settling (where the flocs are strong enough not to float, however the upward force of nitrogen gas entrapment slows down the settling rate) we have had success with increasing mixing prior to the clarifier. This was accomplished by shifting coarse bubble diffused air through one or two diffusers and valving off the others creating rapid mixing (as well as increasing DO concentrations). This had similar impact to the "paddle test" discussed in Chapter 2 in which additional mixing improves settleability.
- Reducing nitrate entry to the final clarifier.
    o Optimizing denitrification in areas such as anoxic selectors or post anoxic zones.
        - Occasionally carbon supplementation may be needed in post anoxic zones to encourage denitrification in these instances.
- Reduce/prevent the formation of nitrate by discouraging nitrification.
    o Reducing the SRT value for BOD removal but not a high enough value for nitrification to occur.
        - If ammonia limits are present in the permit, this is often not a feasible strategy.
    o In instances in which nitrogen is supplemented reducing nitrogen feed (carefully) to avoid nitrification and the formation of nitrate.
- Spray water on the clarifier surface (it helps release nitrogen gas and allows floating sludge to settle) (Richard, 2003).

IN OUR EXPERIENCE, DENITRIFICATION ATTRIBUTED TO STARVATION/ ENDOGENOUS OXYGEN DEMAND IS RARE, HOWEVER POSSIBLE. IF THIS OCCURS, INCREASING THE WAS RATE AND DECREASING THE SRT ARE NEEDED TO REDUCE THE ENDOGENOUS OXYGEN DEMAND.

Denitrification Foam in the Aeration Basin

Regardless of the DO reading, it is important to remember that DO probes are reading "residual DO" outside of the floc. It is possible for simultaneous conditions of aerobic activity on the edges of the floc and anoxic/anaerobic reactions to occur within the center of the floc if DO setpoints are not high enough to keep the flocs fully aerobic (Seifi and Fazaelipoor, 2012). Should nitrate be present, free dissolved oxygen in the interior of the floc depleted, and available carbon present, denitrification may occur in the interior of the floc releasing nitrogen gas in the process. If the mixing in the aeration basin is not high enough to prevent nitrogen gas from becoming entrapped within the flocs, denitrification foaming may occur in the aeration basin. Denitrification foams are often successfully diagnosed by comparing the average floc size in the foam vs. the underlying mixed liquor and if flocs within the foam/scum are significantly larger (generally 1.5x larger per average floc), gas entrapment due to denitrification is suspected (Jenkins et al., 2004).

Figure: 8.16 denitrification foam

IN OUR EXPERIENCE DENITRIFICATION FOAMING IS LIKELY MORE COMMON THAN REALIZED AND OFTEN MIS-DIAG-NOSED.

Control Strategies

(Richard, 2003)

- Increase the DO setpoint and aeration to encourage aerobic interior of flocs.
- Attempt to reduce the oxygen uptake rate by lowering the F/M ratio in the initial contact zone of the aeration basin.
- Increase mixing (if possible).
- Water sprays:
  o This helps improve mixing and allows for entrapped nitrogen gas to escape and the flocs to sink back into the aeration basin.
- Optimize denitrification in intended zones such as the selector or post anoxic selector cells.
- Improve the sludge quality (less filamentous flocs are less prone to floating from denitrification) (Richard, 2003).

8.4 Dispersed Growth

8.4A Causes of Dispersed Single Cell Bacteria (see Chapter 2 for more detail)

(Jenkins et al., 2004)

- High bacterial growth rates in the initial contact zone of the aeration basin.
- Shock Load.
- Slug Load.
- Cation Imbalance.

Figure: 8.17 dispersed growth 100x

Control Strategies for High Dispersed Single Cell Bacteria

(Richard, 2003)

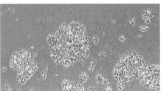

Figure: 8.18 very common dispersed single cell 100x

Figure: 8.19 abundant single cell dispersed 100x

Figure: 8.20 flagellate and dispersed single cell 200x DIC

- Decreasing the oxygen uptake rates and bacterial growth rates in the initial contact zone of the aeration basin by:
  o Increasing the MLSS concentration.
  o Reducing the loading rate (if possible).
  o Putting additional basins online.
  o Step feeding.
  o Optimizing the selector cell performance.

- Reducing the potential for shock loading (if possible) by:

  o Preventing the temperature from passing through ranges such as changes from a mesophilic to thermophilic range.

  o Slow/gradual introduction of a new wastewater stream.

  o Equalization to keep the type of substrate as consistent as possible.

  o Occasionally, mostly in industrial processes, running at a slightly higher MLSS concentration, allowing for bacteria that may be selectively more competitive when different waste streams enter the process ("buffering capacity").

- Reducing the slug loading potential:

  o Enforcement/Implementation of pretreatment standards for industries discharging to POTW.

  o EQ basins and spill/calamity tanks/ diversion of "off spec" waste to ponds/lagoon systems.

- Correcting a Cation Imbalance:

  o High concentrations of monovalent cations (such as sodium and potassium) have the potential to encourage deflocculation whereas multi-valent cations such as calcium, magnesium, and iron are more conductive to floc formation (Sivasubramanian et al., 2021).

    - Some plants have had relative success with avoiding sodium hydroxide for pH control (and using something like magnesium hydroxide in which magnesium is better for flocculation than sodium).

    - Often, cation imbalance can be countered through the addition of flocculating agents/ divalent cations (ferric, ferrous, calcium, magnesium, aluminum) (Sivasubramanian et al., 2021).

IN GENERAL, UNLESS THE TYPE OF WASTEWATER BEING TREATED IS IRREGULAR/ INDUSTRIAL WITH A KNOWN POTENTIAL FOR CATION IMBALANCE, OTHER CAUSES FOR DISPERSED GROWTH ARE MORE LIKELY TO BE DIAGNOSED (SIVASUBRAMANIAN ET AL., 2021B).

8.4B Dispersed Filamentous Bacteria

Figure: 8.21 dispersed Actinomycetes-Mycolata 100x

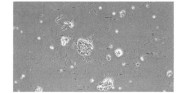

Figure: 8.22 dispersed filaments 100x

Figure: 8.23 dispersed filaments 200x DIC

Background

In general, if a filament type is growing rapidly, it has the potential to grow dispersed in the bulk liquid between the flocs. (See Chapter 2 for further information).

Decreasing Dispersed Filamentous Bacteria: Common Options

- Create an operational change that discourages the growth rate of the problem filament type if possible.

- Use Coagulants or Settling Aids.

  o Consult a trusted chemical vendor.

- Implement Light RAS chlorination.

  o To kill these filaments, "break them up", or help provide a little bit of inhibition to help discourage their growth outside of the floc.

8.4C Dispersed "Fines"/ Dead Cellular Material

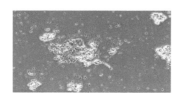

Figure: 8.24 dispersed dead cellular material 100x phase

Figure: 8.25 dispersed dead cellular material 200x DIC

Troubleshooting Steps

- Conduct a microscopic evaluation to determine the most likely cause (see Chapter 2).

Potential Operational Control Strategies to Reduce Dispersed "Fines" / Dead Cellular Material

- Reduce or eliminate the potential cause(s) of inhibition or toxicity.
- Increase the F/M ratio if endogenous conditions are diagnosed as the root cause.
- Improve solids capture from decant or sludge dewatering processes.
- Reduce the concentration of solids entering through upstream or side stream anaerobic processes.
- Use a Coagulant/polymer/settling aid.
  - o Consult a trusted chemical vendor before doing this.

8.5 Foaming in Aerobic Biological Processes

Proper Diagnosis of Foams

Foams cannot be diagnosed reliably from physical observation only and microscopic evaluation is always recommended to determine the root cause(s) of the foam.

Preparing Foam Slides for Microscopy

It is common for foams to be highly concentrated, with TSS concentrations above 1-2% (10-20,00 mg/L). If solids concentrations on the slide are too high, clear distinction between flocs may not be obtained. This becomes particularly important for foams such as denitrification-related foams as the floc size of the foam in comparison to the underlying mixed liquor/biomass is critical for diagnosis (generally, when denitrification is the cause of foaming, the average floc size within the foam is 1.5x or larger than the average floc size of the underlying mixed liquor).

For low power observation of foam samples, a 4:1 dilution or estimated 5,000 mg/L TSS is often a good starting point. If the solids concentration of the foam is smaller, less dilution can be applied and if clear distinction of floc size cannot be obtained with 4:1 dilution, higher dilution may be needed. A slide should be prepped for Gram staining using the diluted sample applied for lower power microscopy.

After low power microscopy observations, the sample should be further diluted to the same general concentrations of a standard sample (<2,000 mg/L) to obtain a flat surface and see filamentous bacteria and other indicator organisms clearly. The same concept of a minimum of 20-30 flocs viewed applies, and in some instances, this may require a second or third slide to obtain a clear "big picture" diagnosis (M. Richard, personal communication).

After high power phase contrast oil immersion observation is completed, Gram staining is the final critical step of evaluation for foam samples.

8.5A Actinomycetes-Mycolata Foams

Microscopic Diagnosis

Actinomycetes-Mycolata foams are officially diagnosed by the visual observation of a significantly higher abundance of Actinomycetes-Mycolata filament types within the foam, compared to the underlying mixed liquor (Jenkins et al., 2004) . Almost all of the Actinomycetes-Mycolata filament types observed in wastewater treatment processes stain Gram positive when healthy. Generally, if these filaments stain Gram negative in a foam they are dead (the filaments often lose their Gram-positive staining reactions once they are no longer alive/viable) (M. Richard, personal communication). Because foaming associated with Actinomycetes-Mycolata filament types is attributed to mycolic acid within the cell walls of these filament types, it is the mycolic acid which is hydrophobic in nature and considered to be the reason for foaming, therefore these filaments can cause/contribute to foaming regardless of if they are viable or not.

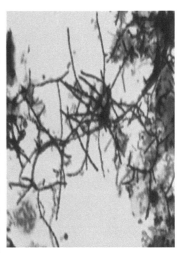

Figure: 8.26 Actinomycetes-Mycolata Gram stain cropped from 1000x

Risks Associated with Actinomycetes-Mycolata Foams

- If the filament growth rate is high enough or if surfactants are also present, Actinomycetes-Mycolata filament foams may billow/ foam over the aeration basins (volcano-like) creating sludge/foam in the surrounding areas of the aeration basin (Jenkins et al., 2004).
  - o In many instances, foam-over events meet criteria necessary for environmental reporting to regulatory agencies.
- Actinomycetes-Mycolata foams often entrap necessary bacteria for treatment within the foam limiting their potential for treatment in biological processes.
  - o If too high of the solids inventory becomes entrapped within the foam, treatment may be compromised or deteriorate (Richard, 2003).

Risk Assessment

From a functional standpoint, it is common particularly in small municipal treatment processes that do not accept outside waste or do not treat a high percentage of industrial wastewater to develop small amounts of Actinomycetes-Mycolata foam on the surface of the aeration basin. Minimal foam accumulation often is impactful on aesthetics only. In certain cases, the signs of risk may be monitored, and the foam may eventually dissipate on its own.

Control of Actinomycetes-Mycolata Foams

- Dispersed Actinomycetes-Mycolata filaments are more susceptible to floating/foaming and in many instances light RAS chlorination has been successful for control.
- A chlorine solution spray at 50 ppm per estimated lb. of biomass in foam 1-2x per day is sometimes successful, according to Dr. Michael Richard's experience in the field.
- Physical removal of foam through a vac truck.
  - o Hauling foam out with sludge for ultimate removal.
  - o Some plants have had success concentrating the foam in a tank, chlorinating the tank heavily, and then slowly bleeding the tank back into the aeration basin.
    - In some instances, vacuum removal is not cost effective, particularly if the foam re-emerges the next day.

- Eliminating potential areas of foam trapping.
- Polymer addition to the RAS (not commonly practiced).
  - o Some plants have reported success with bringing dispersed filaments into the floc where they may be wasted from the process.
- Anti-foam and de-foaming agents.
  - o Oil based defoamers are not advised (potential source for Actinomycetes-Mycolata filaments).
    - • Long term usage of defoamer may worsen problems however defoamer is sometimes needed to prevent foam from spilling over the basin.

CONTACT A TRUSTED CHEMICAL VENDOR FOR DEFOAMER APPLICATION AND USAGE.

Operational Control Strategies for Actinomycetes-Mycolata Foam

- In many instances Actinomycetes-Mycolata foams may be decreased by reducing the SRT value.
  - o It is suspected that the vast genetic diversity of potential Actinomycetes-Mycolata filaments may have a significant impact on their relation to sludge age with some genera and species favoring higher SRT values and others able to compete in lower SRT situations.
- Reduction of FOG at the source.
  - o Grease ordinances.
  - o Permit limits for industrial contributors.
- Primary treatment improvements.

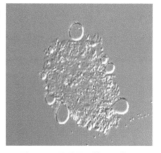

Figure: 8.27 oil on floc 1000x DIC cropped

  - o Primary clarifiers tend to remove more FOG than processes that lack them.
  - o DAF (Dissolved Air Floatation) to remove FOG prior to secondary treatment.
  - o There are case studies in which microscreens may be effective for FOG removal.
- Ceasing acceptance of septage or high-strength waste.
- Reducing areas of septicity in the collection system or treatment plant (if logistically practical).

Background

Operational control and prevention strategies for Microthrix foams are highly similar to Actinomycetes-Mycolata foams (Jenkins et al., 2004).

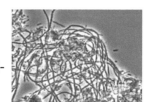

Figure: 8.28 Microthrix cropped from 1000x phase contrast

Additional Growth Factors

- Microthrix filaments tend to compete well at colder temperatures.
- Controlling Microthrix by reducing the SRT value is sometimes effective.
- Some (but not most) plants have reported success with PAX-14 addition.
  - o The factors for why this may work in some instances and not others remain unclear. Potentially the genus or species of the Microthrix filament type may be a factor. (MIDAS database currently recognizes 6 species within the Ca Microthrix genus.)

8.5C Filament type 1863 Foams

Background

In practical experience, type 1863 foams are fairly rare and generally only found in areas in which there is extremely high F/M ratio and fats, oils, and grease (aerated EQ basins, kaldness tanks etc.).

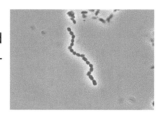

Figure: 8.29 type 1863 1000x phase cropped

Filament type 1863 Foam Control

- Reducing FOG at the source.
- Primary treatment for FOG removal (such as DAF).
- Defoamers may be needed in certain processes.

8.5D Surfactant Foams

Background

Surface-active agents may lower the surface tension of water. At surface tension values of less than 60 dynes/cm surfactant foaming is diagnosed (Jenkins et al., 2004). Surfactant foams possess a soap-sud-like appearance.

Figure: 8.30 surfactant foam

Biodegradability of Surfactants

Surfactants are a broad category classification of chemicals and vary significantly in terms of charge, biodegradability, and inhibitory/toxic impact to wastewater treatment processes. For surfactants that are biodegradable, stabilization tends to be more successful at higher MLSS concentrations, higher SRT values, and higher temperatures (Jenkins et al. 2004). Most biodegradable surfactants are complex and need enzyme activity to be broken down and readily available as substrate for bacteria.

Surfactants and Inhibition/Toxicity

As a general practice, it is considered good operational practice to conduct a thorough microscopic evaluation any time that a surfactant foam is observed within the plant of in the plant effluent. Due to the diversity of surfactants, their impact on the biomass may range from low/insignificant to de-flocculation events, to toxicity and death.

Types of Surfactants

- Anionic Surfactants
- Non-Ionic Surfactants
- Cationic Surfactants

TOTAL SURFACTANT MEASUREMENT INVOLVES TESTING ALL THREE SURFACTANT TYPES.

Operational Control Strategies for Surfactant Foams

- Identify/eliminate source of surfactant entering wastewater process (if possible).
- Neutralize surfactant prior to treatment (dependent on type of surfactant and logistics available).
- Addition of defoamer/anti-foam to minimize foaming in the aeration basin.
  - o In many industrial wastewater treatment processes this may be simply a necessary precaution to avoid tank foam-overs.
- Increasing SRT/ MLSS concentration if surfactant may be biologically degraded.

8.6 Stress, Inhibition, and Toxicity

As discussed previously, stress, inhibition, and toxicity all play a major role in determining which bacteria will compete in a biological wastewater treatment process. Inhibition and toxicity differ in that when inhibition occurs, biochemical reactions are either decreased or temporarily stopped, while toxicity results in actual death of microbes. If "baseline" microscopy assessments are available, especially with fluorescent viability included, a recent "die off" may be easily diagnosed. Note that upon recovery from a toxic event, the following are often encountered:

- A flagellate bloom.
- The emergence of Low DO filament types such as Sphaerotilus and type 1701.
- Dispersed growth and high bacterial growth rates.
- An increase in zoogloea bacteria type abundance (Richard, 2003).

Inhibition is much more difficult to diagnose, and experience has shown respirometry methods such as oxygen uptake rate to be most effective for monitoring.

8.6A Oxygen Uptake Rate (OUR) Measurement
- Basic Equipment Needs
  - Dissolved Oxygen Meter
  - Lab DO Probe and Stirrer
  - Stopwatch
  - 300 mL BOD Bottle
  - Air pump and stone for aerating samples
- Sample Prep
  - Obtain a fresh RAS sample and dilute down to MLSS concentration.
    - Example: *RAS= 9000 mg/L, MLSS= 3000 mg/L* use 100 mL of RAS in the 300 mL BOD bottle
  - "Fed OUR test": Use 200 mL of influent to aeration basin with 100 mL RAS.
  - "Unfed/Baseline test": use 200 mL effluent with 100 mL RAS.
    - Note: In preparing the samples the RAS must be aerated to eliminate initial oxygen demand from not being in aerobic environment.
- Procedure (Rick Marshall, 2021)
  - Aerate the sample to get the DO level high enough (6-8 mg/L) for the test.
  - Fill the BOD bottle with the sample.
  - Start timing after recording the initial DO reading.
  - Record the DO every minute.
  - Stop once DO nears 1 mg/L (at 1 mg/L or less DO can become a limiting factor for uptake rate).
  - Calculate the DO using 3-4 consistent readings.
  - Convert to mg DO/hr. by multiplying by 60.
  - To calculate OUR, the grams of MLVSS (For example if MLVSS is 2,000 mg/L divide by 2.0).
  - OUR PERSONAL PREFERENCE IS USING THE YSI 5100 METER THAT HAS SETTINGS FOR AUTOMATIC OUR CALCULATIONS.
- A Healthy Oxygen Uptake Rate (OUR) Curve
  - The OUR of an activated sludge fed increasing amounts of a nontoxic waste will initially rise with increasing waste additions.

- o Eventually it will reach a maximum oxygen uptake rate in which higher waste concentrations can no longer increase the OUR value.
- Microbial Death
  - o Dr. Michael Richard defines microbial death as when the fed OUR is less than the basal endogenous OUR.

Application

Routine monitoring of oxygen uptake rates in conjunction with measurement of the incoming organic loading rate may help determine when inhibition is occurring. In some instances, these events may be correlated with specific events such as sanitation processes in industrial processes.

8.6B Nitrification Troubleshooting

A common issue encountered for treatment plants that must nitrify to meet ammonia limits is a periodic loss of nitrification. As a starting point, it is recommended to ensure that the following parameters are in place:

- An SRT value of >5 days or higher.
- Adequate HRT values in the aeration basin.
- A pH above 7.
- Residual alkalinity above 50 mg/L.
- DO concentrations of >2 mg/L or higher in the aeration basin.
- The majority of soluble carbonaceous material should be removed (Wisconsin Department of Natural Resources, 2018).

If the above apply and nitrification is still occurring, common issues include:

- Sulfide inhibition.
  - o Sulfide inhibition is highly pH dependent. As the pH increases closer to 8, hydrogen sulfide disassociates to HS- and becomes less inhibitory (Richard, 2003).
  - o Inhibition related to propionic acid and other odd number carbon fatty acids at threshold concentrations (M. Richard, Personal Communication).
- Inhibition related to propionic acid (Pedersen et al., 2009).
- Quaternary ammonium compounds (QACs).
  - o Dr. Clifford Lange recognizes QAC concentrations of >10mg/L in activated sludge solids and >5 mg/L in anaerobic solids as a threshold for the following (Lange, 2020):
    - Reducing surface tension
    - Quat attachment to negatively charged surfaces (including microorganisms)
    - Denaturing the proteins of bacterial cells
    - Interfering with cellular metabolism activities
    - Damaging/disrupting cell membranes
    - Causing cell lysis and microbial death
- QAC BUILDUP IN MIXED LIQUOR PRESENTS A UNIQUE ISSUE OF "LEGACY TOXICITY". WHILE MOST INHIBITION MAY BE "BUFFERED" BY HIGHER MLSS/ HIGHER SRT VALUES, THE OPPOSITE OCCURS WITH QACS. IT IS GOOD PRACTICE TO NEUTRALIZE ALL QACS PRIOR TO BIOLOGICAL WASTEWATER TREATMENT (COMMERCIAL QAC BLOCKING CHEMICALS ETC.).
- Other possibilities include a very high list of metals and other toxic chemicals.
- Often a "needle in a haystack" scenario.

- The most recent priority pollution list may be found at on the EPA website 40 CFR Part 423 Appendix A (The Environmental Protection Agency, 2014).

Nitrite "Lock" (Incomplete Nitrification)

Nitrite lock is a condition in which only the first stage of nitrification occurs and nitrite, an intermediate product of nitrification, remains (Muirhead and Appleton, 2007). Nitrite buildup is undesirable for applications such as disinfection as each mg/L nitrite reacts with 5 mg/L chlorine (Rich, 2003). Additionally, nitrite has the potential to be toxic to aquatic life and is a common reason for WET (whole effluent toxicity) testing failures.

THE SAME PARAMETERS AND LIKELY CAUSES FOR LOSS OF NITRIFICATION APPLY FOR NITRITE "LOCK".

Additional Tools and Control Strategies for Troubleshooting Nitrification

Figure: 8.31 nitrification study

In our experience, a practical starting point is to determine if there is a healthy population of nitrifying bacteria present within the treatment plant. Bioaugmentation through commercial nitrifying bacteria has proven successful in many instances, however if stress exists within the system, added nitrifying bacteria will share the same fate as the current population. The following methods have been proven useful:

- If there are high levels of ammonia in the filtered mixed liquor, obtain a sample, add an air-stone to aerate, and leave overnight. Test the ammonia again in the morning. If the ammonia has been depleted, this indicates that nitrifying bacteria are present however there is not enough "time and numbers" for desired results. In these instances, the addition of commercial nitrifying bacteria to "speed up" the recovery process may be a reasonable choice.

- Influent may be screened for nitrification toxicity by adding a known healthy influent with a BOD:N ratio suitable for nitrification (almost all municipal influent) from a different plant to the RAS at the plant that is not successfully nitrifying.
  - o It is best to try to maintain the ratio of RAS to influent at bench scale, for example, use a total sample volume of 500 mL with 200 mL RAS and 300 mL influent).
  - o Test the raw ammonia in the influent sample compared to ammonia in the filtered mixed liquor after 6-8 hours of aeration.
    - If the ammonia is depleted, this indicates a healthy/stable population of nitrifying bacteria in the RAS and inhibition in the influent at the treatment plant with issues.

- To determine if the inhibition is a result of the RAS ("legacy inhibition"), feeding the influent of known healthy influent to the RAS in question at bench scale may help determine if the issue is within the influent or the biomass.

CAUTION: INHIBITION/TOXICITY PRESENT IN INFLUENT SAMPLES IS COMMONLY INTERMITTENT SO GRAB SAMPLES HAVE THE POTENTIAL TO BE BELOW THE INHIBITION OR TOXICITY THRESHOLD CONCENTRATIONS DEPENDING ON THE TIME OF COLLECTION. IT IS ALSO POSSIBLE FOR DILUTION BELOW THRESHOLD IMPACT TO OCCUR IN COMPOSITE SAMPLES. IDEALLY, AN INFLUENT GRAB SAMPLE TAKEN AT A TIME WHEN YOU OBSERVE SOMETHING ABNORMAL IN THE INFLUENT (I.E. WHITE BILLOWY FOAMING UPON SHAKING) IS RECOMMENDED.

*IN INDUSTRIAL WASTEWATER TREATMENT PROCESSES ADJUSTING PH OR ADDING NUTRIENTS PRIOR TO BENCH SCALE TESTED IS RECOMMENDED.

Practical experience indicates that if effluent ammonia concentrations are fluctuating with a stable BOD:N ratio in the influent that it is likely a stable population of nitrifying bacteria is present with intermittent inhibition.

8.6C Microscopy and DNA Applications

Often, Nitrosomonas may be viewed under the microscope. If high amounts of Nitrosomonas are viewed it is also likely that a stable population of nitrifying bacteria exist but are inhibited from functioning as desired (As Dr. Richard would say "their mouths are closed"). DNA applications such as 16SrRNA community sequencing or qPCR for nitrifying genera read percentages also are useful to determine if a population of nitrifying bacteria is present. Experience has shown that in municipal wastewater treatment processes, nitrification populations of >1% of 16SrRNA reads generally indicate a stable nitrification population while in industrial treatment processes such as meat processing, a significantly higher read percentage of nitrifying bacteria may be needed to nitrify the significantly higher ammonia concentrations in these types of wastewaters.

Ultimately, the decision to add supplemental nitrifying bacteria is case specific and factors such as urgency, oversight by regulatory agencies, cost, and other logistics, as well as potential political factors all play into these decisions. The worst-case scenario is if supplemental nitrifying bacteria are added, and they don't' work because they become exposed to the same fate as the existing nitrifying bacteria population.

Chapter 9:

Microscopy Considerations for Additional Types of Wastewater Processes

9.1 Membrane Bio Reactors (MBR)

9.2 Fixed Film Systems

9.3 Sequencing Batch Reactors (SBR)

9.4 Lagoons and Aerated Stabilization Basins

9.5 Anaerobic Treatment Processes

Background

This chapter will cover microscopy considerations for other types of biological wastewater treatment processes including MBR (Membrane Bio Reactors), SBRs (Sequencing Batch Reactors), Lagoons and Aerated Stabilization Basins, and treatment plants configured for Enhanced Biological Nutrient Removal processes.

9.1 Membrane Bio Reactors (MBR)

In MBR wastewater processes, rather than a clarifier or a DAF responsible for final liquid-solids separation, a filter (membrane) using microfiltration or ultrafiltration is present. MBR processes are common in instances in which the footprint is limited or extremely high effluent water quality is desired (such as for water reuse applications) (Amasci Creative Limited, 2018a). At the time of this writing, MBRs are also gaining popularity in certain industrial treatment processes as they allow for higher SRT values, higher MLSS concentrations, and permeability through the membrane becomes more important than settling/compacting capacities of the sludge (high amounts of filamentous bacteria are generally not problematic in MBR systems).

Similar to tertiary filtration systems, over time fouling of the membranes occurs and once permeability rates decline to a predetermined rate, the membranes must be cleaned using physical and /or chemical methods including backflushing (with or without air), or chemical cleaning with hypochlorite, citric acid, hydrochloric acid, or hydrogen peroxide (Amasci Creative Limited, 2018b).

9.1A Common MBR Foulants and Potential Causes

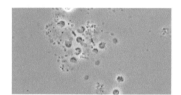

Figure: 9.1 dead cellular material 1000x phase

Figure: 9.2 excessive dispersed growth 200x DIC

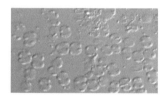

Figure: 9.3 bacteria with excessive polysaccharide cropped from 1000x DIC

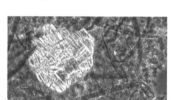

Figure: 9.4 pin floc 100x phase

Figure: 9.5 inert solids cropped 1000x phase

Figure: 9.6 oil on floc 1000x DIC cropped

(Judd, 2012)

- "Fines/ dispersed dead cellular material".
  - o Endogeny/ starvation conditions.
  - o Stress resulting in bacterial death.
- Dispersed single cell bacteria.
- Polysaccharide.
  - o Excessive zoogloea bacteria types.
  - o Shunted growth (producing polysaccharide rather than new "bug bodies") with lack of available nutrients.
- Pin floc.
  - o Stress/ chronic stress.
  - o High SRT/ endogenous conditions/ starvation.

- Inert materials.
  o Insufficient upstream screening *(Judd, 2012)*.

THE PREDOMINANT FOCUS FOR MBR SYSTEMS IS PREVENTING THE GROWTH OF BIOLOGICAL FOULANTS.

9.2 Fixed Film Systems

Fixed film processes (briefly discussed in Chapter 1) differ from traditional activated sludge/suspended growth processes in that the biomass grows on a media such as plastic, rock, or other synthetic solids. There are a wide range of fixed film system types designed for various organic loading rates and various specific goals ranging from full biological treatment to "roughing filters", in which elevated levels of incoming organic acids/readily available substrate are oxidized to "knock down" a portion of the soluble BOD.

Figure: 9.7 Thiothrix (left) type 021N (right) cropped from 1000x DIC

9.2A Microbial Emphasis of Fixed Film Systems

In general, fixed film system effluents are representative of conditions within the media. The microbiology is similar to suspended growth systems and microscopic evaluation methodology is the same as described in this textbook. Common problems encountered in fixed film systems include organic overloading to the process, septicity within the media, or fixed film processes taking up so much of the incoming substrate that downstream processes are impacted negatively.

Sample Locations and Bypassing the Percentage of Flow Around Fixed Films if Desired

In combined fixed film-suspended growth systems, it is recommended to evaluate the fixed film effluent and the suspended growth process individually to obtain an idea of what is occurring within the system. Some treatment processes have the ability to direct the amount of influent that goes to the fixed film process ahead of aeration allowing various % of influent to be bypassed. If septicity/ organic overloading is suspected in the fixed film process, diverting more of the flow around the fixed film process to reduce the oxygen uptake rate in the fixed film process may be warranted to reduce septicity. Additionally, if there is a lack of carbon for processes downstream of the fixed film, either supplemental carbon addition or diverting some flow around the fixed film process may also be desired.

Microbiology Notes

Beggiatoa filament types are most commonly observed in fixed film systems (Wisconsin Department of Natural Resources, 2016). Signs of organic overloading in fixed film systems often include high dispersed single cell bacteria, high zoogloea bacteria type abundance, and an elevated abundance of filament types such as Beggiatoa, Sphaerotilus, type 1701, type 0411, or Thiothrix.

9.3 Sequencing Batch Reactors (SBR)

SBR processes differ from conventional activated sludge treatment systems in that the biological treatment component as well as the final liquid-solids separation phase occur within the same tank (United States Environmental Protection Agency, 1999). SBR processes have a smaller footprint than conventional activated sludge systems and are generally less expensive to construct. Troubleshooting SBR processes may often be especially complicated as a complete understanding of the cycles and the reactions occurring within each cycle is desired.

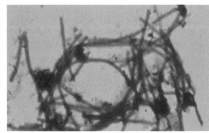

Figure: 9.8 type 0092 Neisser 1000x

9.3A Sampling for Microscopy in SBR Systems

Samples collected for microscopy in SBR systems should be obtained ideally within the final 10 minutes prior to the final settling cycle in which biological treatment is completed. It is very common for treatment plants that contain multiple SBR tanks to have significant differences in their microbiology, so therefore each SBR system should be analyzed and treated individually.

9.3B Troubleshooting SBR Systems through Microscopy Observations

Microscopic evaluation and emphasis for SBR systems is identical to conventional activated sludge systems. A proper microscopic evaluation provides the "big picture" as well as the diagnosis/ root cause of any potential problems. Troubleshooting SBR systems often becomes a little more challenging to diagnose, but sometimes it is also more practical to fix due to the operational flexibility available in these systems.

Common Factors of Operational Flexibility in SBRs
(The International Water Association, n.d.)

- Control of the flow rate during "feed" cycle.
- Anoxic vs. aerobic cycles.
- Duration of cycles.
- Number of cycles per day.
- Post Anoxic cycles for denitrification (if desired).

Notes

In SBR systems it is especially true that microscopic evaluation findings must be used along with process control information. By the nature of SBR processes they resemble ultimate "plug flow" conditions during the filling cycle as all of the influent within the batch is fed at a high rate in most instances. High levels of dispersed growth or signs of organic loading may often be attributed to the F/M ratio being too high during the initial stage or the bleed through of organic acids if an anaerobic/anoxic fill cycle becomes overloaded. Analytical testing of various parameters during stages of the process, ORP measurements, and other tools such as oxygen uptake rate become especially important. ORP measurements may be especially useful if an increase in the ORP value is correlated with nitrification. As an example, some SBR treatment plants have been able to correlate ORP values to ammonia reduction/ nitrification and manually begin the post anoxic cycle to maximize available carbonaceous substrate for denitrification in order to assist with effluent nitrate or total nitrogen limits.

9.4 Lagoons and Aerated Stabilization Basins

Lagoons and Aerated Stabilization Basin (ASB) processes mimic wastewater treatment as it occurs in nature (facultative systems) or with the use of additional oxygen to enhance the growth rates of bacteria and reduce the footprint needed for treatment. Lagoon systems are particularly common in rural areas for smaller municipal treatment systems and ASBs are common in industrial wastewater treatment processes such as pulp and paper mill applications.

Lagoons and ASBs are similar in that the final cell is typically unaerated allowing for settling of the flocculated biomass (accomplishing final liquid-solids separation). Rather than sludge being thickened and either returned to the front of the system or wasted, the sludge settles to the bottom "benthic" layer where, in most instances, natural anaerobic digestion of the solids occurs. Successful digestion/stabilization of the settled solids results in decreasing the total sludge yields from approximately ½ lb. solids to ¼ lb. solids that eventually need to be removed (typically accomplished through dredging).

9.4A Operational Control of Lagoons and Aerated Stabilization Basins

The basic fundamentals of wastewater treatment and the same microbiology methods apply to these treatment processes, however there are some specific considerations that can be made by operational personnel depending on treatment schematic:

- Primary Treatment (more common in ASB processes).
    - o Operation of the primary clarifier(s).
        - In many pulp and paper applications, septic sludge blankets in primary clarifiers may be a major source of organic acid formation which may impact microbiology (organic acid filaments, zoogloea bacteria types predominant etc.).
- EQ basin/Spill tank.
    - o Some (limited) plants have the ability to store "off spec" wastewater temporarily to be blended into the system.
- Chemical Addition.
    - o Maintaining alkalinity/ pH.
    - o Chemical phosphorous removal.
- Nutrient Addition (more common in industrial wastewater treatment plants).
    - o Nitrogen.
    - o Phosphorous.
    - o Micronutrients (only if needed).
- Operational Control.
    - o Parallel vs. series operation.
    - o Effluent recycling flow adjustments (some processes).
    - o Taking cells offline/ "resting".
    - o Adjusting aeration/ location of aerators.
    - o Step feed.
        - It helps to distribute loading evenly, reducing the oxygen uptake rate and bacterial growth rates at the front end of the process.

Bioaugmentation in ASB systems

In many ASB treatment configurations, since there is no recycling of solids (i.e. RAS line) and the BOD values are significantly higher than municipal treatment systems, this may create unique challenges. In many instances, step feed configurations have been implemented to assist spreading the loading more evenly throughout the lagoon, however there are certain applications in which supplemental bacteria added to the front end of the biological treatment process may help to reduce the initial F/M ratio, allowing for selection of bacteria that may settle better in the final cell. These instances are case by case and long-term operational costs vs. capital costs should be evaluated, however in any treatment system meeting, compliance goals are the main objective.

Side Stream Bioaugmentation

In some industrial wastewater treatment processes, rather than adding supplemental bacteria to the entire process, it may be more economical to target specific production streams that are known to be high in BOD concentrations. There are instances in which using an added oxygen source (commonly calcium nitrate) in addition to bacteria that compete at very high F/M ratio may convert soluble organic material to particulates which may then potentially settle out in processes such as a primary clarifier.

9.4B Lagoon System Limitations

Depending on the climate, certain areas experience very cold weather and freezing in which bacterial growth rates/rates of treatment decrease significantly. It is very difficult for many lagoon systems to nitrify, especially in colder climates, during the winter season (United States Environmental Protection Agency, 2011). Additionally, growth of algae present challenges for effluent BOD and TSS should algae proliferate in areas such as the final settling cell. Algal growth occurs due to the presence of phosphorous and (to a slightly lesser extent) nitrogen, favoring sunlight, high hydraulic retention time, and often the benthic feedback of nutrients from bottom sludge layers. Due to increasingly stringent nitrogen and phosphorous limits, many lagoons are either being converted into conventional activated sludge processes or fixed film processes are added after the lagoon prior to discharge to improve nitrification performance.

Lagoons are inherently limited by the treatment area (footprint) and ambient temperatures. While operating costs are significantly reduced in lagoon processes due to lack of WAS handling, every system eventually needs to dredge solids as sludge accumulation over time results in the benthic feedback of nutrients and organic acids, as well as reduced space for treatment capacity.

9.4C Microscopy Considerations for Lagoons and ASBs
(Richard, 2003)

Most lagoon systems contain multiple cells with one or more cells in series or parallel configuration followed by a final settling cell. To gain an understanding of what is occurring in these systems and to use the microscope for troubleshooting purposes, conducting microbial examinations of each cell within the system is recommended. It is fairly common in lagoon systems to see signs of high organic loading rates, low dissolved oxygen, and septicity in the first cell, with the microbiology resembling "cleaner/more stabilized water" throughout different stages of the process. A representative sample taken at the outfall of each cell (ideally through a sampling port) is recommended (Richard, 2003).

Microscopy for lagoon systems follows the same principles as for activated sludge samples, however, it is common for the suspended solids concentrations to be low. Often, one must concentrate the solids, or allow them to settle, to obtain enough for representative microscopy. For example, in a lightly loaded municipal treatment lagoon system, obtaining a sample of around 500 mL and allowing it to settle overnight or over the course of several hours may be needed. In rare instances after prolonged settling, the supernatant may remain cloudy, or algae will float to the surface of the sample. In these instances, it is recommended to evaluate the settled material once it is compacted and then mix the sample allowing for a representative perspective of dispersed growth. The same general concept of evaluating a minimum of 20-30 flocs applies to both analysis techniques (Richard, 2003).

Microscopy Focus for Troubleshooting Lagoon Systems

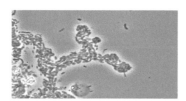

Figure: 9.9 fingered zoogloea cropped 1000x phase contrast

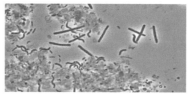

Figure: 9.10 Flexibacter and Spirilla cropped from 1000x phase contrast

Figure: 9.11 fibrous 200x DIC

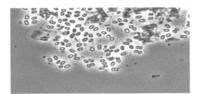

Figure: 9.12 anaerobic sulfur bacteria
1000x phase contrast

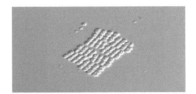

Figure: 9.13 Thiopedia anaerobic
sulfur bacteria 1000x DIC cropped

- The rank and abundance of filamentous bacteria morphotypes associated with low dissolved oxygen and septicity (elevated organic acid concentrations).
  - o These types of filaments should decrease as the water quality improves throughout the lagoon system. Should these filaments increase after decreasing in a previous cell this is a strong indication of organic acids associated with benthic feedback from the sludge layer.
- The abundance of inert and fibrous materials.
  - o Abundant non-microbial particles that would generally be expected to settle out raise the potential for short circuiting in the system.
- Anaerobic sulfur bacteria.
  - o In lagoon systems, photosynthetic anaerobic sulfur bacteria may oxidize sulfide. Intra-cellular sulfur granules are often observed in these bacteria and when present at high abundance often create a pink to slightly purplish tint to the water.
  - o These anaerobic sulfur bacteria are beneficial as they reduce sulfide related odors, however, they may negatively impact effluent quality contributing to color or turbidity.
    - Presence of these bacteria indicates sulfide from the influent or sulfide released due to benthic feedback.
- Algae and Algal Predator Cycles.

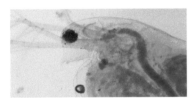

Figure: 9.14 daphnia brightfield

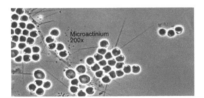

Figure: 9.15 green algae 200x

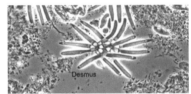

Figure: 9.16 green algae 200x phase

Figure: 9.17 Pediastrum

Figure: 9.18 green filamentous

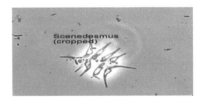

Figure: 9.19 Scenedesmus

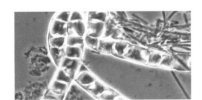

Figure: 9.20 Uronema 1000x

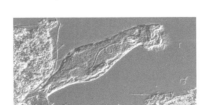

Figure: 9.21 rotifer 200x DIC

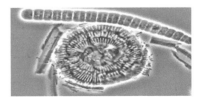

Figure: 9.22 cyanobacteria filament
and diatom

- It is common in lagoon systems for an imbalance to occur which leads to a cycle of algal blooms, followed by the proliferation of algal predators. Eventually, once the algal predators starve or complete their life cycles, they die and re-release organic matter and nutrients causing algae to repopulate (Richard, 2003).
    - Common algae predators are daphnia, other crustaceans, and rotifers.
    - Algae potentially encountered in lagoon systems include green algae, brown algae (diatoms), and blue-green algae.
        - Blue-green algae are especially prone to high nutrient loadings, septicity, and high BOD concentrations (Richard, 2003).

Algae Impacts
- An algae concentration greater than $3\text{-}5 \times 10^5$/mL generally causes an effluent BOD concentration greater than 30 mg/L (Richard, 2003).
- Elevated algae in the effluents contributes to the total suspended solids concentrations.
- Changes in pH (increases up to a pH of 9).
- DO depletion during the evening hours when algae use oxygen and DO supersaturation during the daylight hours when algae use carbon dioxide and release oxygen (Richard, 2003).
- Periods of algae proliferation and die off (see the above paragraph).
- Additional production of sludge from algae and algae predator life cycles/ cell lysis contribution of BOD.

Common Algae Control Methods
(Hill, 2016)
- Limiting HRT values when possible.
    - Taking cells offline that aren't needed for treatment during warmer periods of the year.
    - Effluent recirculation.
- Hold-and-Release Strategies.
    - Discharging periodically as your permit allows/ not discharging during periods of high algal growth.
- Selective Discharge.
    - Discharging from the cell with the best quality.
    - Subsurface discharge (discharging water beneath the algae layer on the surface).
- Shade/ sun-blocking methods.
- Chemical treatment.
    - Consult a regulatory agency prior to any applications.
- Barley straw.
- Improving mixing/turbulence:
    - Helps to strip CO_2 to the atmosphere.
    - Potential for a turbulent surface to reduce sunlight penetration from algae.
    - Potential to help break up mats of algae from forming.
- Ultrasonic devices (Hill, 2016).

CO2 Reduction

- Dr. Michael Richard believes that if CO2 levels are controlled through the consumption of alkalinity in nitrification without the denitrification step to recover alkalinity then algae will not bloom. In this case, the CO2 available for algae growth is limited to that which can be transferred from the air.

9.4D Lagoon and ASBs: Common Engineering Upgrades

- Advanced Integrated Pond Systems (AIPS) (Spuhler, 2020).
    - These systems contain a truly anaerobic cell where methane is generated prior to the aerated lagoon cells.
        - Advantages include:
            - o Reducing aeration demand.
            - o Reducing CO2 (part of digester biogas).
            - o Reducing organic loading.
            - o A higher potential for nitrifying during colder months as the majority of carbonaceous organic material is removed through the upstream anaerobic cells.
- Introduction of a Step Feed.
- Control of Parallel vs. Series Operation.
- Effluent Recirculation.
- DAF (Dissolved air floatation) for final liquid- solids separation.
- Addition of fixed film processes to increase the amount of available biomass.
- Temperature control (generally not cost effective but used in some post-nitrification processes).
- Diffused aeration added to the bottom layer for mixing and clear interface of the benthic bottom layer and aerated portions.
- Lagoon Covers.
    - o Reduces sunlight.
    - o Retains heat.
- "Biolac."
    - o Conversion of an overloaded lagoon to an extended aeration activated sludge process.
        - Common in industrial wastewater treatment plants.

9.5 Anaerobic Treatment Processes

Background

Anaerobic treatment is a process that occurs in 4 steps, ultimately converting organic material into biogas (i.e. methane and carbon dioxide) along with a low cellular yield of new biomass. Free dissolved oxygen is inhibitory for true anaerobes. A simplified way of looking at anaerobic treatment is in 2 steps: the breaking down of organic material into the smallest pieces (i.e. acetic acid) followed by Methanogenesis, in which acetic acid, hydrogen, and carbon dioxide are then converted into biogas. The early steps of anaerobic treatment involve the production of organic acids/volatile fatty acids which are discussed in great detail in the chapters regarding aerated activated sludge treatment. The microbes responsible for fermentation are generally bacteria that are hardy, fast growing, and that compete well even in influent wastewater, collection systems etc., whereas methanogens are archaea which are slow-growing and sensitive to a high variety of potential stresses.

The four actual steps of anaerobic treatment include 1) Hydrolysis (of polymers, fats, oils, and grease, and polysaccharides), 2) Acidogenesis (anaerobic oxidation of amino acids, sugars, fatty acids, and alcohols), 3) Acetogenesis (formation of acetic acid, hydrogen, and carbon dioxide from intermediate products such as volatile fatty acids), and 4) Methanogenesis as described in the paragraph above.

Advantages and Disadvantages of Anaerobic Treatment Processes
(Rumbaugh, 2014)

Advantages
- Low biological solids yield (methane gas is the predominant end product).
  - 6-8x less biomass produced on average.
- Energy produced may be harvested for reuse.
- Low macronutrient demand due to low biomass yield.
- Ability to treat highly concentrated/ heavily organically loaded wastes.
- Treatment of FOG (fats, oils, and grease) produce high biogas yields (Rumbaugh, 2014).

Disadvantages
- Methanogens (archaea) are slow-growing and sensitive to many stresses.
- High capital cost for construction.
- If sufficient alkalinity is not present, the pH may decrease below ranges that methanogen can compete in.
  - Alkalinity supplementation is needed in various applications.
- Temperature should ideally be maintained to limit daily fluctuation.
- While organic material (COD, BOD) is removed due to low biomass yield, assimilation of nutrients into bacteria is low, leaving high remaining nutrients.
  - In an aerobic BNR (biological nutrient removal) configuration, carbon is needed for processes such as denitrification and enhanced biological phosphorous removal.
- Odor potential.
- Micronutrients such as copper are critical, and while they are typically present in most wastes, if those micronutrients are not present, micronutrient supplementation is recommended.
- Common operational problems (discussed later within this chapter) (Rumbaugh, 2014).

9.5A Common Anaerobic Treatment Process Configurations
(United States Environmental Protection Agency, 2015)
- Anaerobic Lagoons
  - Requires a large footprint.
  - Common in industrial processes such as meat processing.
- Anaerobic Sludge Blanket Reactors
  - Upflow anaerobic sludge blankets (UASBs)
  - Expanded granular sludge beds (EGSBs)
  - Anaerobic baffled reactors (ABRs)
- Anaerobic Filter Reactors (United States Environmental Protection Agency, 2015)

9.5B Common Problems Encountered in Anaerobic Processes
(Wisconsin Department of Natural Resources, 2018)

- Variations in organic loading/ lack of upstream equalization.
- Temperature fluctuations.
- Buildup of solids within the system over time, reducing the available treatment capacity.
- pH decreases ("sour" digester).
- Hydrogen sulfide production.
  - o Odor/Safety.
  - o Inhibitory to methanogens at elevated concentrations.
- Foaming caused by:
  - o A lack of mixing.
  - o Elevated volatile acids (lowers surface tension).
  - o Filamentous bacteria such as Microthrix or Actinomycetes-Mycolata types which foam even when dead (generally do not grow naturally in anaerobic systems however present with flows such as WAS).
  - o Surfactant chemicals.
  - o Dead bacteria.
- Organic overloading, leading to the washout of biomass.
- Toxicity/Inhibition:
  - o Quaternary Ammonium Compounds.
  - o Nickel.
  - o Iron.
  - o Peracetic acid.
  - o Surfactants.
  - o Others.

Common Operational Troubleshooting Guidelines for Anaerobic Processes
(Wisconsin Department of Natural Resources, 2018)

- Feeding at a consistent organic loading rate.
- Regularly wasting solids.
- Maintaining adequate volatile acid: alkalinity ratios (i.e. <0.5).
- Ferric addition to precipitate excess sulfide (sulfide >50 mg/L may cause inhibition).
- Optimizing mixing and temperature control.
- Avoiding overloading the processes (i.e. DAF primary treatment etc.).

9.5C Anaerobic Microscopy

At the time of this writing, there is very little credible literature available for microscopy on anaerobic processes. The following information is passed on from Dr. Michael Richard based on 40 years of experience monitoring anaerobic systems as well as coupled anaerobic/aerobic treatment systems (M. Richard, Personal Communication).

Low Power (10x, 20x) Considerations

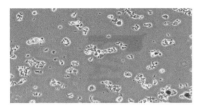 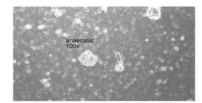 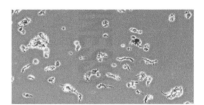

Figure: 9.23 anaerobic flocs low dispersed growth 100x phase

Figure: 9.24 anaerobic high dispersed 100x phase

Figure: 9.25 anaerobic common dispersed 100x phase

Anaerobic flocs are generally smaller than the aerobic flocs encountered in activated sludge processes. To successfully conduct anaerobic microscopy, it is recommended to establish "baseline" conditions in which anaerobic treatment performance is high and compare it to periods in which anaerobic treatment performance (i.e. soluble COD removal) is not as high. It is typical to observe dispersed single cell growth even in systems that are functioning well, however high levels of dispersed growth often correlate with reduced anaerobic efficiency. Under periods of stress, we have observed "broken up" flocs and it is suspected that in general, larger flocs are attributed to methane gas entrapment (gas being produced faster than mixing allows gas to be driven from the flocs). This is commonly observed in foaming events in which organic loading/lack of mixing is diagnosed as the root cause of the foaming (M. Richard, Personal Communication).

High Power (100x Oil Immersion) Considerations

The techniques for low power and high power are the same as traditional wastewater microscopy requiring the "hard smash" for high power observation. Samples should be diluted to generally below 1000 mg/L total suspended solids to properly view flocs, filaments, and other components at high power (M. Richard, Personal Communication).

Anaerobic Filaments

There are four common anaerobic filament morphotypes observed in anaerobic systems. The exact causes of these filaments are unclear at this time; however, they appear to correlate with elevated organic acid concentrations (as plants with lesser organic acid concentrations generally have less of these filaments).

Anaerobic morphotype "A"

- A thin (0.4 µm) and generally short (<50 µm) filament that stains gram positive and is very closely related to Haliscomenobacter morphotypes. Cell septa andsheaths are not visible within this morphotype.

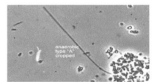

Figure: 9.26 anaerobic type A 1000x phase

Anaerobic morphotype "B"

- Approximately 0.9-1.1 µm in diameter. Septa are not visible; however sheaths are often observed within this filament type (generally around the tip). Anaerobic type "B" filaments stain Gram positive and based on experience are generally the most common anaerobic filament type observed in highly loaded systems.

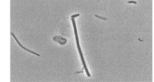

Figure: 9.27 anaerobic type B 1000x phase

Anaerobic morphotype "C"

- Approximately 0.7-1.1 µm in dimension, square-rectangular cell shape with visible septa. Filaments resemble morphotype 0914/0803 however often have a slightly transparent appearance. These filaments stain Gram negative.

Figure: 9.28 anaerobic type C 1000x phase

Streptococcus morphotype

- Approximately 1-2.5 μm in diameter with a discoid-"hockey-puck" shape and visible cell septa. No sheath. Filaments resemble Nostocoida limicola III types. A Gram-positive staining reaction is commonly observed.

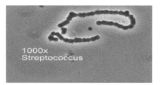

Figure: 9.29 Streptococcus 1000x phase

Others

Figure: 9.30 Flexibacter 1000x DIC

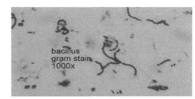

Figure 9.31 bacillus gram stain cropped from 1000x

Flexibacter and Bacillus morphotypes at high abundance are generally indicators of elevated organic acid concentrations in anaerobic systems.

"Incidental" Filaments

Often various filamentous bacteria are introduced to anaerobic treatment processes through being present in the WAS stream. In many conventional municipal aerobic digesters, it is common to see fragments and generally dead/unhealthy filaments that were previously healthy in the mixed liquor or the WAS. None of the commonly recognized filamentous morphotypes associated with filamentous bulking events compete well in anaerobic systems (M. Richard, Personal Communication).

Foaming Associated with Microthrix and Actinomycetes-Mycolata Filament Types

Neither Microthrix nor Actinomycetes-Mycolata filaments compete well in anaerobic systems, however these filaments may often cause/contribute to foaming if they are present at significant abundance. Actinomycetes-Mycolata filament types are hydrophobic (prone to foaming) due to the mycolic acid within their cell walls. This acid is present even after the death of the filament and foaming may still persist. A similar phenomenon is observed in Microthrix filament types. When observed through microscopy it appears common for Actinomycetes-Mycolata and Microthrix filaments to lose their Gram-positive staining characteristics when they are dead. Using fluorescent microscopy for dead/alive viability staining also appears to support the theory of these filaments losing their Gram-positive properties based on our experience. In practice, the best long-term control practice to discourage Actinomycetes-Mycolata and Microthrix foaming in anaerobic processes is to reduce their presence through the feed WAS via upstream treatment modifications. While not ideal, defoaming and anti-foam applications are often   successful in preventing these types of foams from overflowing anaerobic treatment vessels. Note that defoamer/anti-foam does not address the root cause, but it may limit the risk of tank overflow/ reportable incidents in many scenarios (M. Richard, Personal Communication).

9.5D Bioaugmentation Considerations for Anaerobic Processes

Bioaugmentation (the addition of supplemental microbes) has been commonly practiced in anaerobic treatment systems. Based on my personal experience, it is my belief that incidents in which this may be beneficial are rare and likely limited to steps in which hydrolysis, acidogenesis or acetogenesis are a limiting factor for methane formation. There are likely a few exceptions with very tough/difficult to ferment wastewater. In practice, it appears that acid forming bacteria are far more stable and reliable than methanogens. Generally, either a lack of methanogen population or factors that inhibit the growth of methanogens are more likely for anaerobic treatment process failures. Unfortunately, methanogens are not easily grown in the lab and supplemented as commercial products, and the added bacteria described as anaerobes function for fermentation purposes but do not generate methane.

In certain circumstances we have seen successful bioaugmentation by introducing sludge with a known healthy and readily available population of methanogens to a system that lacks methanogens. Note that for these instances to be successful, the outlying conditions that inhibited the previous methanogens must no longer be present in order for the methanogens to "catch". Dr. Richard has observed that methanogen bacteria appear to remain viable in a non-ideal place (i.e. a truck) for approximately 24 hours (M. Richard, Personal Communication).

Chapter 10:

DNA Applications in Wastewater

Background

Beginning at the turn of the 21st century, genetic testing capabilities have progressed and continue to progress at a high rate. From a wastewater microscopy prospective, the biggest revelation has been the vast range of genetic diversity of bacteria found in different types of wastewater treatment processes. From a technical standpoint, the major change here is that we now know that we are identifying wastewater microorganisms such as filamentous bacteria by "morphotypes", rather than actual genus and species (which requires more advanced genetic testing applications). The good news from an operational perspective is that these recognized morphotypes have a strong track record linked to operational performance going as far back as the early 1980s. The clarifications needed are technical in that it is not valid to assume a genus or species based only on microscopy observations (with very few exceptions, but even here caution is needed).

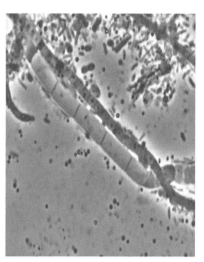

Figure: 10.1 type 021N multiple phase contrast 1000x cropped

"What's in a Name"

To keep wastewater microscopy consistent with scientific nomenclature it is important to explain when italics are used and when they are not warranted. When referring to a microorganism by morphotype no italics are needed as this is a general description based on the appearance of the microorganism. In wastewater microscopy we are linking morphotypes (not genus or species) to causes. When we refer to the genus and species, italics are present for clarification purposes (American Society for Microbiology, n.d.). Due to the naming of the morphotypes, there is some overlap, and it is possible for both italics and non-italics to be used in various scenarios. For example: "Haliscomenobacter" is used when we are referring to the (broader) Haliscomenobacter morphotype vs. "*Haliscomenobacter*" which is specific to the Haliscomenobacter genus (*Haliscomenobacter hydrossis* is then a species of the Haliscomenobacter genus that fits the description of the Haliscomenobacter morphotype). Simply put we are only identifying by morphotype when using microscopy and italics should not be used unless there is context to the actual genetic properties (genus level or lower) of the microorganism.

10.1 Changes from Earlier Literature and Reasons Why

10.1A Explanations for Updated Training Methods

Elimination of the Dichotomous Key/ De-emphasis on Staining for Most Morphotype Identifications

- It is very easy to get on the "wrong path" as the key was highly dependent on staining reactions.

    o Staining reactions can often be attributed to the chemistry of the wastewater; often in industrial processes staining reactions can be highly variable.

    o Staining reactions are highly dependent on the technique of the lab tech and improper decolorizing can easily lead to inaccuracies (Sutton, 2006).

    o Due to the high genetic diversity within the recognized morphotypes it is likely many genera with the same morphotype have different staining characteristics (Speirs et al., 2019).

Why Gram and Neisser Staining Remain Essential

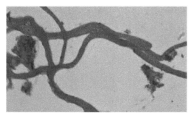

Figure: 10.2 Nostocoida limicola III with irregular gram staining

Figure: 10.3 Actinomycetes-Mycolata Gram stain 1000x

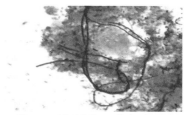

Figure: 10.4 Microthrix Gram

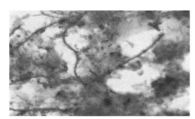

Figure: 10.5 type 0581 cropped

Figure: 10.6 PAOs Neisser 1000x

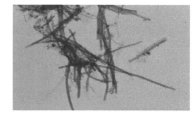

Figure: 10.7 type 0092 Neisser

- Identification of Microthrix must be gram positive (or else it can be confused with morphotype 0581).
- Healthy Actinomycetes-Mycolata filaments are almost always Gram positive.
- Filament type 0092 is always Neisser positive, and staining is required for proper identification.
- Traditional PAOs (Polyphosphate Accumulating Organisms) stain deeply Neisser positive (purple).

De-Emphasis on Filament Length and the Location of Filaments

- While this is relevant for many morphotypes, there are many exceptions to these guidelines and the visibility of cell septa, sheath, cell shape and diameter take priority for identification.
- Depending on growth conditions most filaments can grow dispersed in solution should the growth rates be high enough, based on our experience in the field.

De-Emphasis on Filament Shape

- Filamentous morphotypes can be variable as to their shape (straight vs. smoothly curved, etc.)
  o Based on our experience with classroom training this often causes confusion.
- The visibility of cell septa, sheath, cell shape, and diameter take priority for identification.

De-Emphasis on Attached Growth Presence/Absence

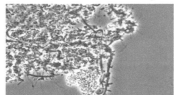

Figure: 10.8 Nostocoida limicola and type 0914/0803 filaments with attached growth

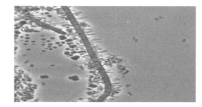

Figure: 10.9 type 021N phase contrast attached growth 1000x cropped

- Almost all filamentous morphotypes can incur attached growth if they are present in the system long enough for bacteria to adhere to them.
- It remains true that high SRT filaments more often contain attached growth, however assigning attached growth presence/absence for morphotype identification is irrelevant and often leads to misidentification.

De-Emphasis on PHB Granules

- All filamentous bacteria have the ability to store PHB. It remains true that PHB granules are more commonly observed in certain filaments (particularly if they are growing fast), however using PHB granules for identification may lead to confusion (Speirs et al., 2019).

10.1B Changes to Recognized Filamentous Morphotypes with Explanations

"Sphaerotilus natans" has been shortened to Sphaerotilus as there are fourteen known species within the Sphaerotilus genus (Sphaerotilus natans is only one of these species). Also the genus Leptothrix is commonly associated with the Sphaerotilus morphotype (Nielsen et al., 2009a).

- Additionally, it is highly probable that unclassified Proteobacteria phylum members may also possess Sphaerotilus morphology under the proper growth conditions.

"Haliscomenobacter hydrossis" has been shortened to "Haliscomenobacter" as there are 10 known species within the Haliscomenobacter genus at the time of this writing (Dueholm et al., 2021). In addition, modern guidelines de-emphasize attempting to link potential operational causes to Haliscomenobacter morphotypes in the absence of in-house/operational testing parameters that may help alleviate error.

- Haliscomenobacter morphotypes have been linked to the Bacteroides and Chloroflexi phylum (Speirs et al., 2019).
- Tax ID 89374 (unclassified Saprospiraceae family; same family as Haliscomenobacter) appears to be present as often as, if not more than, the actual Haliscomenobacter genus when comparing microscopy and DNA testing results.

PLEASE REFER TO CHAPTER 6: HIGH POWER MICROSCOPY OBSERVATIONS, FOR POTENTIAL CAUSES ASSOCIATED WITH HALISCOMENOBACTER.

"Thiothrix I and Thiothrix II" have been shortened to "Thiothrix" as there are 46 known species within the actual Thiothrix genus (Dueholm et al., 2021).

- The previous descriptions were based on diameter. However, from a practical standpoint, it is more important to associate these descriptions together as to not "dilute" the abundance associated with potential causes.
  - Additionally, Thiothrix and type 021N are no longer classified with low nitrogen availability. This remains possible, however the listing of low nitrogen availability as a presumed cause of Thiothrix and type 021N has led to high amounts of confusion.

ANTHRONE TESTING IS RECOMMENDED TO DETERMINE NUTRIENT AVAILABILITY FOR BACTERIA.

"Nostocoida limicola I and Nostocoida limicola II" are combined as a single morphotype and now referred to as "Nostocoida limicola I and II".

- This change can be made by simply extending the diameter range of the filament morphotype description. In addition, as with the new Thiothrix morphotype, this allows for simplification of microscopy and in addition avoids "dilution" of emphasis or cause in association to filament abundance.

NOSTOCOIDA LIMICOLA I AND II MORPHOTYPES ARE RECOGNIZED TO SPAN ACROSS A WIDE RANGE OF PHYLUM, GENERA, AND SPECIES AT A GENETIC LEVEL HOWEVER THE ASSOCIATED GROWTH CAUSE OF ELEVATED ORGANIC ACIDS IS STILL WARRANTED (NIELSEN ET AL., 2009B).

"Nocardioforms/Nocardia" are no longer recognized and are replaced by the Actinomycetes-Mycolata morphotype.

- In wastewater treatment processes such as refineries and paper mills it is suspected that Actinomycetes-Mycolata may grow on organic acids.
- In municipal processes or food manufacturing processes in which fats, oils, and grease are present, the conversion of the fats, oils, and grease to long chain fatty acids under septic conditions appears to be the predominant and generally most likely cause for Actinomycetes-Mycolata filament growth.

TAKING INTO CONSIDERATION GENETIC PROPERTIES, THE MAJORITY OF ACTINOMYCETES-MYCOLATA FILAMENTS COMMONLY FOUND IN WASTEWATER PROCESSES ACROSS THE UNITED STATES AND CANADA APPEAR TO BE UNCLASSIFIED TAX ID MEMBERS OF THE ACTINOBACTERIOTA AND ACIDOBACTERIOTA PHYLUM (WITH A FEW EXCEPTIONS AND RECOGNIZED GENERA SUCH AS GORDONIA).

"Type 0803" is no longer recognized as a low F/M filament. This morphotype has been combined with type 0914 and is now referenced as "type 0914/0803"as FISH probes have found these filament types genetically similar (Nielsen et al., 2009a).

- Previous literature classifying type 0803 as low F/M also included a description of the filament type as growing dispersed and it is not common for filaments growing as a result of low F/M to grow in dispersed form indicating a previous likely contradiction.

FILAMENT TYPE 0914/0803 APPEARS TO BE MOST OFTEN ASSOCIATED WITH THE CHLOROFLEXI PHYLUM OR THE PROTEOBACTERIA PHYLUM AND IS RECOGNIZED TO CONTAIN BROAD GENETIC DIVERSITY (NIELSEN ET AL., 2009B).

"Type 0041 and 0675" have been combined as "type 0041/0675".

- In practice the only differentiation of note between these filament types was the diameter size and it is easy to adjust the diameter size of the morphotype and combine them together to simplify microscopy.
- The recognized growth cause for type 0675/0041 is higher SRT and often accompanying a low F/M ratio at the end of the aeration basin or biological treatment process.

FILAMENT TYPE 0675/0041 IS ASSOCIATED WITH BOTH CLASSIFIED AND UNCLASSIFIED MEMBERS OF THE CHLOROFLEXI AND PATESCIBACTERIA PHYLUM.

"Microthrix parvicella" has been shortened to "Microthrix" as the Microthrix genus consists of 6 recognized species (including Microthrix parvicella and Microthrix calida) (Dueholm et al., 2021).

- The overall causes remain the same (oleic acid and other long chain fatty acids formed from septic fats, oils, and grease), however it is incorrect to assume all Microthrix morphotypes are Microthrix parvicella species.

10.2 Notable Limitations of Wastewater Microscopy

10.2A Subjectivity Considerations

An important factor for consideration in any testing procedure is practical applications of the results leading to information that may lead to process control decisions. In addition to practical applications, potential limitations must always be considered. One of the biggest challenges with wastewater microscopy is the subjective nature of morphotype recognition, as several factors are at play including fitting broad ranges of genera and species into morphotype categories. There are also many factors that may influence the morphological traits of microorganisms, including the type of substrate, growth rate, and the presence of "stress/inhibition". Despite our best efforts to simplify microscopy, the reality is that filamentous bacteria and other indicator organism morphotypes do not always fit neatly into pre-defined morphotype trait descriptions allowing for various interpretations depending on who is performing the analysis. When in doubt, do not "force fit" a morphotype identification, simply skip to the next filament in view. For even the most advanced and proficient experts in this field (likely a single-digit number of people in North America) by nature of the subjectivity there is potential for minor differences such as classifying similar looking morphotypes differently. To counter this inherent "noise" it is important to note that the overall goal of wastewater microscopy is obtaining a "big picture" diagnosis and therefore should slight variances be encountered by different "experts" they should ultimately come to the same conclusion of the overall microscopy diagnosis.

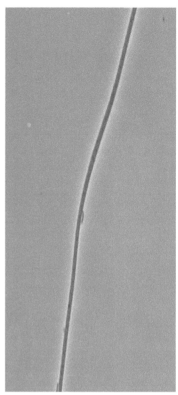

Figure: 10.10 non-recognized morphotype

Another practical tool for morphotype identification is simply "birdwatching"- recognizing a morphotype through repetition. If an individual is serious about becoming proficient in wastewater microscopy, obtaining a mentor who has vast experience analyzing samples from a wide array of different types of treatment plants is beneficial. Additionally, to help overcome the naturally subjective nature of wastewater microscopy applications over time, experts in this area understand certain trends and correlations (i.e. which morphotypes commonly occur together) as well as using all of the data obtained from the microscopic evaluation to develop an "overall big picture" assessment.

Equally, if not more important than the table for morphotype descriptions may be obtaining a high-quality poster which may be placed next to the microscope for "birdwatching-like" comparison. When comparing what is visible on the microscope camera monitor to the poster my 6-year-old daughter does a fairly good job of morphotype identification. Many plants have also benefitted from custom made posters more specific to what is generally present within their systems, as in many instances specific plants incur reoccurring issues of the same nature and often microscopy can be optimized by "looking for specific things that may trigger operational changes."

10.2B Common Microscopy Errors

From a morphotype identification standpoint, common issues encountered include not having access to the proper equipment needed, insufficient knowledge of microscope operation (such as mis-alignment of phase contrast rings), insufficiently cleaned lenses and other parts of the microscope where light is transmitted for view, slides not prepared properly or pressed properly at high power microscopy in which a filament type can be viewed clearly, and other flaws in techniques such as staining, preparing slides for viewing, and general operation of the microscope. A filament needs to be viewed on an even plane in a flat and thin preparation as well as clearly be in focus to accurately describe morphological traits.

10.2C Training Considerations

Due to the naturally subjective nature of wastewater microscopy, finding a competent trainer/mentor may be challenging. Learning how to interpret wastewater microscopy consistently and accurately from a wide range of different types of treatment applications is a process that may take years and several hundred samples with the oversight of a mentor before competency is reached. Even after mastery of skills, improving microscopy assessment can be thought of as a life-long, never-ending challenge to improve.

In many trades, the 10,000-hour rule applies, and a strong case can be made that proficiency of wastewater microscopy fits into this category. Also, it is not only the time allocated to the trade, but also the quality of the work/ learning the "fundamentals". (A good sports analogy is that "practice doesn't make perfect; rather perfect practice makes perfect").

It is unwise to take a 2-day class and then consider yourself an expert in wastewater microscopy. It is also important that the trainer is qualified and proficient in the knowledge that is passed down. As an example, for companies that offer microscopy services with a wide range of lab techs, the quality of the microscopy evaluation is often specific to the lab tech performing the analysis. Additionally, by nature training knowledge may often be "diluted". For example, if someone is trained, then becomes the trainer, then trains the next person it is only natural that some of the intricacies of the craft are missed in each series.

ON A POSITIVE NOTE, MASTERY OF FULL-SCALE MICROSCOPY APPLICATION IS OFTEN NOT NEEDED TO USE THE MICROSCOPE FOR PROCESS CONTROL APPLICATIONS, ESPECIALLY AS TRAINING CAN BE ADJUSTED TO MEET THE SPECIFIC NEEDS OF EACH PLANT AND COMMON CIRCUMSTANCES/ THINGS TO "LOOK FOR".

10.2D Other Natural Limitations of Microscopy

Other natural limitations of microscopy reflect the chapter topic of DNA and the genetic diversity that is present amongst different types of wastewater treatment processes as well as the wide range of genetic diversity that is common in most of the morphotypes of importance in wastewater. There are high amounts of bacteria present in wastewater processes that may not be readily recognized through morphological characteristics that may have the potential to give us additional information about the wastewater treatment process. For example, Nitrosomonas and Nitrobacter morphotypes are the only types of nitrifying bacteria that may readily be viewed through phase contrast microscopy (Jenkins et al., 2004). We have learned over time that the role of Nitrobacter in most biological wastewater treatment processes is relatively low or in most instances entirely insignificant with Nitrospira commonly responsible for the majority of NOB (nitrite oxidizing bacteria) functions (Mehrani et al., 2020). Since Nitrospira is not readily viewed through phase contrast, DNA testing can be beneficial when troubleshooting nitrification issues. (For example, if there is a stable population of nitrifying bacteria present that are simply inhibited or if nitrifying bacteria are entirely lacking).

Microscopy is one specific piece of the puzzle and, based on knowledge gained since the late 1970s, we have successfully been able to correlate many morphological traits of microorganisms with causes that occur within the treatment plant. As DNA research has improved, we also have the ability to learn about the characteristics of a sample based on other bacteria that may not have readily distinguishable morphological characteristics. A good example of this was using DNA in addition to microscopy for a plant that was struggling to nitrify. We suspected septicity (specifically propionic acid formation) as inhibitory to nitrification and while no specific testing for propionic acid was conducted, 16S rRNA sequencing showed a high percentage of reads of bacteria that ferment organics into propionic acid helping to support the theory. Subsequently, through ORP measurement, it was learned that the influent entered a large unmixed zone prior to entry to the

Figure 10.11 Nitrosomonas cropped from 1000x phase contrast

SBR treatment processes in which high amounts of sludge had settled out. Installing a mixer in this area kept the solids in suspension, reduced the septicity/fermentation, and the plant has not struggled with nitrification since this change occurred.

With increasingly stringent permit limits and an increasing amount of treatment plants modified for enhanced biological nutrient removal, we are limited in some regards for using microscopy as the sole means to help understand the intricacies of enhanced biological phosphorous removal as not all PAOs (polyphosphate accumulating organisms) possess the traditional deeply Neisser positive staining characteristics. Also, we are learning that many of the genera capable of enhanced biological phosphorous removal may also function in different ways (denitrification, glycogen accumulation) likely explaining why some plants have difficulty consistently sustaining luxury uptake of phosphorous.

In summary, it is always important to be open minded from a scientific perspective of new technologies and how and when they may be used to help in regard to troubleshooting treatment processes as well as gaining a greater understanding of the complexities of each system.

10.3 Notable Limitations of DNA Sequencing (16SrRNA)

Television crime dramas such as CSI have likely helped elevate the perception of DNA capabilities to unrealistic expectations. As with microscopy and all other testing procedures, it is important to acknowledge the fundamental limitations that occur. At the time of this writing (and into the foreseeable future) we do not view DNA testing (16SrRNA) as a replacement for microscopy, but rather as an additional tool that may be used in conjunction in the appropriate circumstances.

Figure: 10.12 DNA testing Aster Bio Report

A Brief Description of 16SrRNA testing

The basic concept is that 16SrRNA sequencing is community analysis (archaea or bacteria) that measures the percentage of overall reads obtained by measuring ribosomal RNA interactions with a primer. Based on patterns within these interactions, sequences are obtained which must meet 98.65% probability to constitute a read. Reads are presented to the lowest denominator of accuracy available (Rizal et al., 2020).

In bacterial taxonomy, the rankings in ascending order are most often classified as species, genera, families, orders, classes, phyla, and domain. The potential causes and functionality of bacteria are generally more precise as lower reads (i.e. genera or species) are obtained (Garg, 2016).

10.3A Read Percentage vs. Abundance

A common misconception encountered when interpreting 16SrRNA results is that the percentage of overall reads is representative of the abundance as viewed under the microscope. While there are often trends and correlations that may be achieved, certain genera may have multiple strands of RNA (causing interference with elevated reads) as well as the factor of high DNA present in exocellular polymers/polysaccharides which inherently contain high amounts of DNA (Johnson et al., 2019). As an example, it is common for genera such as Zoogloea or Thauera to contain 15-20% of total reads and be ranked common in abundance through microscopy while certain filaments above 2-3% of total reads may be ranked excessive through microscopy and diagnosed as responsible for major bulking events. Lastly, other suspected interferences include growth rates (more DNA produced when bacteria growing) and emerging evidence of horizontal gene transfer interference being higher than originally thought.

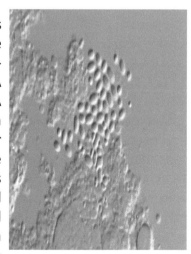

Figure: 10.13 zoogloea cropped from 1000x DIC

10.3B Variable Morphological Characteristics of many Genera and Species

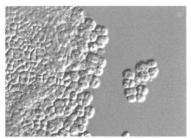

Figure: 10.14 tetrads cropped from 1000x DIC

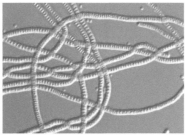

Figure: 10.15 Nostocoida limicola III DIC 1000x

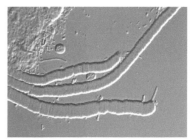

Figure: 10.16 Nostocoida limicola III cropped 1000x DIC

Many genera and species of bacteria often have variable morphological traits, and their physical characteristics may change in response to their environment, growth conditions, and other (at this time often poorly understood) factors (Dueholm et al., 2021). The majority of genera that possess filamentous morphology may also exist in other forms such as tetrads, clusters of bacteria, or in single cell form. A good example here is reads in the Acinetobacter genus, which is recognized to have over 90 individual species, some (but not all) of which may possess type 1863 filament morphology. Therefore, seeing the Acinetobacter genus may or may not be representative of type 1863 filament presence. Another example is the Defluviicoccus genus, which contains 51 recognized species (mostly unnamed) and may likely be responsible for bulking events based on high percentage reads if they possess Nostocoida limicola morphology, but they may also be fairly harmless in most instances (with the same read percentage) if present in tetrad morphology within the flocs (Dueholm et al., 2021). Simply put, due to most filamentous bacteria having variable filamentous morphology (sometimes or usually, but not always in filamentous form) microscopy is needed for supplemental confirmation of the morphological properties of the bacteria.

10.3C Viability Aspects

When bacteria die, DNA is rapidly degraded by other bacteria as a food source with varying amounts of time that DNA stays in the system to be measured (Li et al., 2017). A good example of this challenge is a plant that had bulking episodes with filament type 021N (in this instance per DNA testing, it was suspected to be Ideonella genus with type 021N morphology). Two paralell plants processed the same influent and had highly closely related genetic properties with the notable exception of Ideonella. Subsequently, RAS chlorination had been applied aggressively to one of the plants and not to the other. Microscopy revealed that the plant with the aggressive RAS chlorination predominantly showed a dead type of 021N filament morphotypes while the other plant showed predominantly healthy 021N morphotypes. In both instances type 021N filaments were interfering with settling, however the more aggressive chlorine dose was shown to have killed the majority of the filaments but not actually break them up (so the dead filaments were still impacting the SVI value). If only looking at DNA Ideonella would not have been suspected to be the cause of the settling issues as it was likely dead and did not register in the testing per this theory.

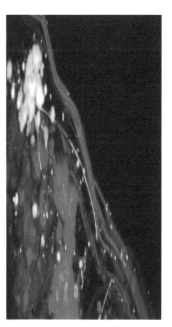

Figure: 10.17 dead filaments fluorescent 1000x cropped

10.3D Lack of Floc Structure Assessment and Microscopy Observations

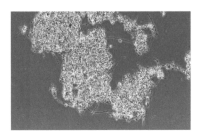

Figure: 10.18 strong flocs abundant filaments

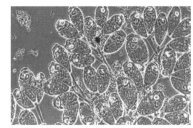

Figure: 10.19 stalked ciliates 100x phase contrast

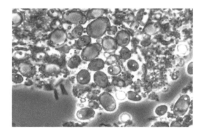

Figure: 10.20 yeast 1000x phase contrast

In every plant there is importance in separating "conditions" from "problems". For example, in many industrial wastewater treatment processes, due to the natural presence of elevated organic acid concentrations, abundant filamentous bacteria are often present and simply a factor of "you are what you eat". As described in earlier chapters, floc strength and structure are equally, if not more important in terms of SVI values as filament abundance as the stronger and heavier the floc, the more filaments that may be supported without increasing SVI values. Therefore, just because a particular filament type has a high percentage of DNA reads, this doesn't always necessarily mean that the filament is creating problems. Similarly, in microscopy, this reflects the same reason not to offer any operational advice without learning more about the intricate details of the facility, situation, and logistics that apply of what (if any) operational actions may be warranted.

Of note protozoa, metazoan, and other advanced higher life form organisms such as yeast are not reflected in DNA assessments as they are not bacteria or archaea. Subsequently, if doing DNA testing, it is important to clarify if bacteria and archaea, of simply one or the other is being scanned for. For most aerobic biological treatment processes bacteria only is sufficient for "big picture' diagnosis however low amounts of archaea are generally present as well.

10.3E Unclassified Reads, Problematic Filament Types for DNA Matches, and More

Making correlations of "who's there" based on comparison of DNA and microscopy is difficult and despite comparing DNA analysis to microscopy for hundreds of samples the author has found that there are often times when correlations simply cannot be achieved (and even if correlations are suspected, they need to be proven through methodology such as fluorescent in-situ hybridization to be validated). Further complicating this is that due to the high diversity of bacteria present in most samples and the non-linear association of abundance as viewed under the microscope vs. The percentage of reads, an unknown filament type candidate could potentially make up 4% of total DNA reads and be undistinguishable vs. other genera with higher read percentages that are not as abundant per microscopy, effectively "lost in the shuffle".

Also, with current technology, a lot of reads do not reach taxonomic levels such as genus or species (i.e. a tax ID # with a known family or perhaps higher up read and no further detail) although this is improving at a rapid pace and expected to continue to improve. Often, there is still value obtained in DNA sequencing as general characteristics at the family level or higher may sometimes apply. In our experience, unclassified reads (not reading to the genus or species level) appear to be commonly prevalent in Actinomycetes-Mycolata filament types, which often are recognized as unclassified reads in the Actinobacteriota or Acidobacteriota phylum or filament type 0675/0041, 1851, 0092, 0581, and 0914/0803 which commonly fall into unclassified Chloroflexi (Speirs et al., 2019). Additionally, many filaments with type 021N or Thiothrix morphological traits are believed to fall into unclassified Proteobacteria reads (certain families are more likely to be filaments per theory however difficult to determine if the high read percentage is a floc former, single cell bacterium, or a filament).

Nostocoida limicola filament type reads have very high potential genetic diversity and Nostocoida limicola morphological traits are believed to be recognized in the Planctomycetes, Firmicutes, Actinobacteriota, and Chloroflexi phylum (Nielsen et al., 2009a). Over time, some correlations have been proven, some remain theories, and others are likely difficult to discover and may likely fall into unclassified reads.

Discrepancy in Database Libraries

Type strains of 16S rRNA gene sequences for most bacteria and archaea are available on public databases such as NCBI however, the quality of these sequences is often not validated. Because of this, secondary databases are commonly used for microbe classification. Recognized databases include EzBioCloud, Ribosomal Database Project, SILVA, and MIDAS (Balvočiūtė and Hudson, 2017). While similar, there are many discrepancies in the naming of microbes with potential to obtain different results/names depending on which secondary database is used for classification. Based on our experience in the United States we have had the best correlations using Aster Bio for DNA sequencing and then using the MIDAS database. Later within this chapter some inconsistencies in naming on the tables may be seen due to various databases used comparing microscopy to DNA results.

Discrepancy in 16SrRNA Sequencing

It is important to note that not all 16SrRNA sequencing is the same. Results may vary depending on which region(s) of the 16SrRNA gene are tested for and there are also other factors such as the platform method of sequencing (MiSeq, Illumina, etc.) (Zhang et al., 2018; Quail et al., 2012). Different regions of the 16S rRNA gene are more likely to produce bacteria reads as opposed to archaea reads (Bukin et al., 2019). While most conventional aerobic wastewater treatment processes are predominantly compromised of bacteria, archaea may play significant roles (especially in certain industrial wastewater treatment plants) and by the nature of the testing, archaea reads are generally not reliable when targeting regions (typically V3 or V4) most typically correlated with bacteria.

Anaerobic Challenges in 16SrRNA Sequencing

Methanogens are typically the most explored microorganism type in anaerobic sequencing as they are needed for the conversion of volatile fatty acids/organic acids to methane and other end products. Commonly, when anaerobic processes fail, bacteria still produce enough volatile fatty acids/organic acids through fermentation and the methanogen population is not efficient enough to convert these to methane and other end products (also producing a low anaerobic cell yield through "treatment"). Because 16S rRNA sequencing is catered specifically to either bacteria or archaea and both are important in anaerobic treatment processes ideally both should be targeted to interpret anaerobic results, according to Dr. Paul Cambell of Aster Bio. A qPCR test is also available to determine the percentage of bacteria vs. archaea in a sample which then can be used to scale these readings- effectively requiring 3 tests for a representative test. Also, while we continue to learn more about methanogens and their biodiversity in wastewater treatment processes the science in these areas is rapidly emerging as we continue to learn.

10.3F Pricing, Turn-Around Time, and Practical Usage in Operations

DNA testing has increasingly become more cost effective and at the time of this writing testing costs ranged between $250-$800 dollars for 16SrRNA sequencing with a turn-around time ranging from a couple of days to several months depending on the lab being used. In some instances, qPCR assays (quicker turn-around times and cheaper costs) are effective tools and while they don't provide community analysis, they may help quantify a problem microorganism (i.e. monitoring Zoogloea, Thauera, Nitrosomonas, Nitrospira, or perhaps a certain distinguishable filament type such as Microthrix). By the nature of DNA testing, there is always a grey area in knowledge based on defining what is practical for operational purposes (such as: if I see something on the testing, I do something differently at the plant) vs. academic purposes. We view this as case specific with the biggest factor being that to justify the testing (or any testing for that matter), the information obtained needs to be worth the value of the test and the available turn-around time for results.

Lastly, the vast amount of information that can be made available through genetic testing needs to be converted into a form that is usable, understandable, and practical from an operational perspective or it may be difficult to determine how to utilize it successfully. Practical experience shows that this is best served by analyzing trends rather than one-time samples. If testing is conducted such as monitoring nitrification diversity activity the ultimate end goal is low effluent ammonia concentrations, which may be met with a range of percentage reads of nitrifying bacteria depending on factors such as how much ammonia needs to be oxidized to nitrate, and temperature/ metabolic rate considerations. Therefore, success is determined by low effluent ammonia rather than a certain percentage of reads and each plant's "success" read abundance may be different. The same theory applies to monitoring processes such as enhanced biological phosphorous removal. While over time certain percentage reads may loosely correlate with enhanced biological phosphorous removal performance, factors such as inhibition, the multiple roles of many PAO genera (i.e. some can act as denitrifying bacteria or GAOs as well), temperature, metabolic rates, and more, success is more easily defined by testing effluent orthophosphate removal rates rather than percentage reads of genera capable of enhanced biological phosphorous removal. Lastly, another factor of consideration in monitoring enhanced biological phosphorous removal processes is that the weight percentage of bacteria as phosphorous may vary. For example, genera such as Microthrix are not classified as PAOs (they do not release orthophosphate under anaerobic conditions) however they are believed to store a higher concentration of phosphorous than most traditional floc forming bacteria (Dueholm et al., 2021). Simply put, the complexity of all of the external factors poses challenges in correlating the percentage of DNA reads to "success".

As with microscopy, the frequency of genetic testing should always be practical. A good case can often be made (as with microscopy- high power assessments) that unless there is a major change noticed in treatment plant performance, any intervals of testing more than 1x per week may have diminishing returns of value.

10.4 qPCR Testing Functionality

DNA testing using qPCR techniques involves using a selected primer to target various genetic sequences (Kralik and Ricchi, 2017). Recently, at the time of this writing qPCR testing has been used widely for COVID-19 applications in the medical field.

10.4A Applications and Limitations of qPCR Testing Capabilities

In specific instances, qPCR testing can be advantageous, especially if the goal of the test is to only monitor one particular microbe or set of microbes. qPCR testing is used in wastewater treatment commonly for instances such as monitoring Zoogloea, Thauera, or nitrifying bacteria activity (Blackwood et al., 2005). Turnaround time for qPCR testing is quick (it can be completed within a few hours) and pricing is becoming more economical. Limitations are that qPCR only targets a specific microbe set and it is common for genera to have multiple primers needed for detection. If the proper primer is not chosen, the test result will not show relative abundance of the targeted microbe type of interest.

10.5 The Functional Roles of Genera and Other Areas of Interest in Wastewater Treatment Processes (Referencing the MIDAS Database)

10.5A Polyphosphate Accumulating Organisms (PAOs)

By definition, polyphosphate accumulating organisms consist of a higher percentage (by weight) of phosphorous than traditional wastewater bacteria. In the process of enhanced biological phosphorus removal, bacteria store VFAs under anaerobic conditions while releasing orthophosphate, converting the stored VFAs to Polyhydroxyalkanoates (PHA). Upon entering the aeration basin, they oxidize PHA, taking up additional amounts of phosphorous (known as "luxury uptake" in the process). (Tarayre et al., 2016). Systems that acquire a stable population of PAOs remove higher amounts of phosphorous biologically than traditional treatment systems.

While science is still emerging in this field, a good amount of information has been obtained in regard to the functionality and genetic diversity amongst bacteria that are classified as PAOs.

Table of PAO Genetic Characteristics (Dueholm et al., 2021)

Figure: 10.21 PAOs 100x Neisser

Genus	Phylum	Species	Notes
Accumulibacter	Proteobacteria	57	Typically one of the primary genera responsible for enhanced biological phosphorus removal. Also, some species can switch between PAOs and GAOs.
Tetrasphaera	Actinobacteria	33	Some species may also be involved in denitrification. Some (but not all) possess Nostocoida limicola morphotype but rarely cause bulking issues
Obscuribacter	Cyanobacteria	6	Unknown/ ongoing research.
Corynebacterium	Actinobacteria	16	Unknown/ ongoing research.
Halomonas	Proteobacteria	20	Typically small straight or curved rod-shaped cells. Some species can grow in a filamentous form.
Dechloromonas	Proteobacteria	79	Rods/ coccobacilli. Sometimes form microcolonies. Species within this genus vary in PAO capabilities.

10.5B Nitrifying Bacteria

Nitrifying bacteria are responsible for the oxidation of ammonia to nitrite, and then nitrate in a two-step process. Bacteria classified as AOB (ammonia oxidizing bacteria) convert ammonia to nitrite and NOB (nitrite oxidizing bacteria) then convert nitrite to nitrate, which is the final end product of nitrification (Dueholm et al., 2021).

Research has shown that it is very common for Nitrosomonas to be the predominant AOB and Nitrospira to be the predominant NOB present, however depending on circumstances it is important to note other genera capable of roles in nitrification (see table below (Dueholm et al., 2021)).

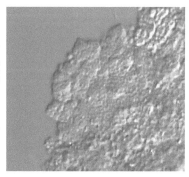

Figure: 10.22 Nitrosomonas cropped from 1000x DIC

NOTE THAT NITROBACTER, WHICH MAY BE VIEWED THROUGH PHASE CONTRAST MICROSCOPY IS BELIEVED TO TYPICALLY PLAY A LOW OR INSIGNIFICANT ROLE FOR NITRITE OXIDATION IN MOST TREATMENT PROCESSES (NITROSPIRA TENDS TO BE THE PREDOMINANT NOB IN MANY SYSTEMS). OMITTED FROM THIS TABLE ARE ARCHAEA, OF WHICH A FEW GENERA ARE BELIEVED TO BE CAPABLE OF NITRIFICATION FUNCTIONS (DUEHOLM ET AL., 2021).

Table of Nitrifying Bacteria Genetic Characteristics (Dueholm et al., 2021)

Genus	Phylum	Species	Function
Brocadia	Planctomycetes	5	AOB and NOB
Nitrosomonas	Proteobacteria	85	AOB
Nitrosospira	Proteobacteria	5	AOB
Nitrobacter	Proteobacteria	3	NOB
Nitrospira	Nitrospirae	37	NOB and variable AOB
Nitrotoga	Proteobacteria	3	NOB
Tax ID 206379	Nitrosomonadaceae family. Proteobacteria phylum.	Unknown	Suspected AOB

AOB= Ammonia Oxidizing Bacteria NOB= Nitrite Oxidizing Bacteria

TAX ID 206379 (UNCLASSIFIED) OF THE NITROSOMONADACEAE FAMILY (SAME FAMILY AS NITROSOMONAS) APPEARS TO BE COMMONLY OBSERVED IN COMMUNITY ANALYSIS AND IS SUSPECTED TO FUNCTION AS AN AOB.

10.5C Glycogen Accumulating Organisms (GAO)

Glycogen Accumulating Organisms are able to store glycogen in anaerobic environments to utilize in later aerobic biological processes. There exists a complicated and rather poorly understood relationship between GAOs and PAOs in regard to competition for substrate in enhanced biological phosphorous removal processes at the time of this literature (Dueholm et al., 2021).

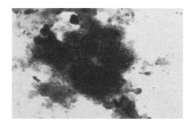

Figure 10.23 GAOs Neisser

Genus	Phylum	Species	Notes
Accumulibacter	Proteobacteria	57	Many species are variable GAOs (can also be PAOs).
Competibacter	Proteobacteria	111	N/A
Contendobacter	Proteobacteria	14	N/A
Defluviicoccus	Proteobacteria	51	Some can possess Nostocoida limicola morphotype in filamentous form.
Micropruina	Actinobacteria	9	Cells appear as clusters or pairs with cocci shape.
Propionivibrio	Proteobacteria	49	N/A

10.6 Genetics vs. Microscopy: Confirmed and Hypothetical Relationships for Filament Types

Disclaimer

Many of the theories listed below have not been validated at the time of this writing and many of the potential correlations are likely to be eventually proven true, while a significant amount will likely be discredited upon further research. These findings are based on a study in 2020 and 2021 comparing 16SrRNA sequencing (using Aster Bio lab) to microscopy conducted by Ryan Hennessy with findings from over 100 plants using activated sludge processes with a mixture of plant types, including municipal plants (conventional and modified for enhanced biological phosphorous removal), and various industrial treatment processes (paper mills, food processing, agriculture, refineries, soft beverage, leachate, and others).

Morphological Category Discrepancies

Due to the similarities of many recognized morphotypes from this text certain morphotypes have been combined for the purpose of this study. Correlations that are theoretical in nature (based on the current database for Ryan Hennessy's microscopy using Aster Bio DNA 16SrRNA results) will be marked and correlations confirmed by MIDAS will also be mentioned in this text.

10.6A Sphaerotilus/ Type 1701 Morphotype Correlations and Candidates

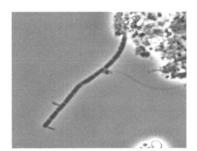

Figure: 10.24 type 1701 phase contrast

Genus or Lowest Read Obtained	Variable filament type y/n	Recognized # of species	MIDAS confirmed as filament capability y/n	RH-Aster Bio filament candidate y/n	Notes of Importance
Sphaerotilus	Yes	14	Yes	Yes	Gammaproteobacteria class. Proteobacteria phylum.
Leptothrix	Yes	32	Yes	Yes- however appears to correlate more with Thiothrix morphotypes.	Gammaproteobacteria class. Proteobacteria phylum.
Curvibacter	Unknown	8	No	Potentially	Gammaproteobacteria class. Proteobacteria phylum.
Chryseobacterium	Yes	126	Yes	Potentially	Bacteroides phylum.

10.6B Haliscomenobacter Morphotype Correlations and Candidates

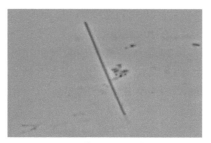

Figure: 10.25 Haliscomenobacter phase cropped 1000x

Genus or Lowest Read Obtained	Variable filament type y/n	Recognized # of species	MIDAS confirmed as filament capability y/n	RH-Aster Bio filament candidate y/n	Notes of Importance
Haliscomenobacter	No (Always filamentous)	10	Yes	Yes	Saprospiraceae family, Bacteroides phylum.
Tax ID 89374	Unknown	Unknown	Unknown	Yes-variable	Unclassified Saprospiraceae family. Bacteroides phylum.
Chryseobacterium	Yes	126	Yes	Potentially	Weeksellaceae family. Bacteroides phylum.
Tax ID 1936988	Unknown	Unknown	Unknown	Potentially	Bacteroides phylum. Saprospirales order.
Tax ID 1937961	Unknown	Unknown	Unknown	Potentially	Haliscomenobacteraceae family. Bacteroides phylum.
Longilinea	No (Always filamentous)	10	Yes	Likely	Anaerolineaceae family. Chloroflexi phylum.
Leptolinea	No (Always filamentous)	65	Yes	Likely	Anaerolineaceae family. Chloroflexi phylum.
Flexilinea	No (Always filamentous)	7	Yes	Likely	Anaerolineaceae family. Chloroflexi phylum.
Tax ID 292628	Unknown	Unknown	Unknown	Potentially	Anaerolineaceae family. Chloroflexi phylum.

10.6C Thiothrix/type 021N Morphotype Correlations and Candidates

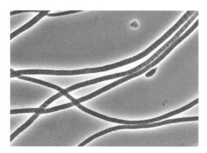

Figure: 10.26 type 021N cropped from 1000x phase contrast

Genus or Lowest Read Obtained	Variable filament type y/n	Recognized # of species	MIDAS confirmed as filament capability y/n	RH-Aster Bio filament candidate y/n	Notes of Importance
Thiothrix	No (Always filamentous)	46	Yes	Yes	Gammaproteobacteria class. Proteobacteria phylum.
Leptothrix	Yes	32	Yes	Yes	Gammaproteobacteria class. Proteobacteria phylum.
Thioalkalispira-Sulfurivermis	Unknown	1	Unknown	Potentially	Gammaproteobacteria class. Proteobacteria phylum.
Neomegalonema	No (Always filamentous)	5	Yes	Not observed in Aster Bio reads.	Alphaproteobacteria class, Proteobacteria phylum.
Dokdonella	Listed as non-filamentous	21	No	Strong Correlations.	Gammaproteobacteria class. Proteobacteria phylum.
Ideonella	Unknown	22	Listed N/A but description mentions filamentous potential.	Likely	Gammaproteobacteria class. Proteobacteria phylum.
Aquabacterium	Unknown	22	Unknown	Likely	Gammaproteobacteria class. Proteobacteria phylum. More of a type 021N morphotype candidate than Thiothrix morphotype.
Reyranella	Unknown	13	Unknown	Suspected variable filament.	More commonly correlated with type 0961 morphotypes. Occasionally suspect Thiothrix II types. Alphaproteobacteria class, Proteobacteria phylum.
Tax ID 1236	Unknown	Unknown	Unknown	Suspected variable filament types within tax ID.	Gammaproteobacteria class. Proteobacteria phylum.
Tax ID 80840	Unknown	Unknown	Unknown	Suspected variable filament types within tax ID.	Burkholderiales order, Proteobacteria phylum.
Tax ID 1224	Unknown	Unknown	Unknown	Suspected variable filament types within tax ID.	Unclassified Proteobacteria phylum.

Tax ID 80864	Unknown	Unknown	Unknown	Suspected variable filament types within tax ID.	Betaproteobacteria class. Proteobacteria phylum.
Tax ID 119060	Unknown	Unknown	Unknown	Suspected variable filament types within tax ID.	Burkholderiaceae family, Proteobacteria phylum.
Tax ID 2689614	Unknown	Unknown	Unknown	Suspected variable filament types within tax ID.	Gammaproteobacteria class. Proteobacteria phylum.
Bellilinea	No (Always filamentous)	6	Yes	Filament candidate.	Anaerolineaceae family, Chloroflexi phylum. Possibly similar to type 0092 morphotype.

10.6D Nostocoida limicola III/ type 021N Morphotype Correlations and Candidates

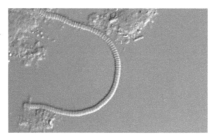

Figure: 10.27 Nostocoida limicola III cropped from 1000x DIC

Genus or Lowest Read Obtained	Variable filament type y/n	Recognized # of species	MIDAS confirmed as filament capability y/n	RH-Aster Bio filament candidate y/n	Notes of Importance
Ca Nostocoida	No (Always filamentous)	1	Yes	Not Observed	Isosphaeraceae family, Planctomycetota phylum.
Thiothrix	No (Always filamentous)	46	Yes	Yes	Gammaproteobacteria class. Proteobacteria phylum. Correlations with type 021N morphology.
Streptococcus	Yes	31	Yes	Yes	Firmicutes phylum.
Trichococcus	Yes	1	Yes	Yes	Firmicutes phylum.
Defluviicoccus	Yes	51	Yes	Yes	Alphaproteobacteria class, Proteobacteria phylum. Confirmed tetrad forming capabilities.

Amaricoccus	Unknown	55	No	Yes	Alphaproteobacteria class, Proteobacteria phylum. Confirmed tetrad forming capabilities.
Plasticicumulans	Unknown	7	No-Unknown	Likely	Gammaproteobacteria class. Proteobacteria phylum.
Gemmata	Unknown	22	No-Unknown	Possibly	Planctomycetota phylum.
Ca *Alysiosphaera*	No (Always filamentous)	13	Yes	Not Observed.	Alphaproteobacteria class. Proteobacteria phylum.
Tax ID 112	Unknown	Unknown	Unknown	Potentially	Planctomycetota phylum.
Tax ID 203682	Unknown	Unknown	Unknown	Potentially	Planctomycetota phylum.
Tax ID 2066434	Unknown	Unknown	Unknown	Potentially	Alphaproteobacteria class. Proteobacteria phylum.
Tax ID 1914233	Unknown	Unknown	Unknown	Potentially	Alphaproteobacteria class. Proteobacteria phylum.
Tax ID 468	Unknown	Unknown	Unknown	Potentially	Gammaproteobacteria class. Proteobacteria phylum.
Tax ID 1765324	Unknown	Unknown	Unknown	Potentially	Isosphaeraceae family. Planctomycetota phylum.
Tax ID 666507	Unknown	Unknown	Unknown	Potentially	Planctomycetota phylum.
Tax ID 666505	Unknown	Unknown	Unknown	Potentially	Planctomycetota phylum.

10.6E Type 0961 Morphotype Candidates and Correlations

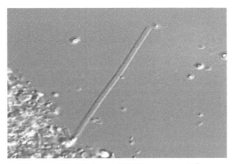

Figure: 10.28 type 0961 cropped from 1000x DIC

Genus or Lowest Read Obtained	Variable filament type y/n	Recognized # of species	MIDAS confirmed as filament capability y/n	RH-Aster Bio filament candidate y/n	Notes of Importance
Reyranella	Unknown	13	Unknown	Yes (suspected variable)	Alphaproteobacteria class. Proteobacteria phylum.
Tax ID 1224	Unknown	Unknown	Unknown	Potentially	Proteobacteria phylum.
Tax ID 80840	Unknown	Unknown	Unknown	Potentially	Betaproteobacteria class. Proteobacteria phylum.

10.6F Type 0914/0803 Morphotype Candidates and Correlations

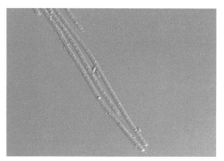

Figure: 10.29 type 0914_0803 cropped 1000x DIC

Genus or Lowest Read Obtained	Variable filament type y/n	Recognized # of species	MIDAS confirmed as filament capability y/n	RH-Aster Bio filament candidate y/n	Notes of Importance
Acidovorax	Listed as non-filamentous	32	No	Yes	Gammaproteobacteria class. Proteobacteria phylum.
Anaerolinea	No (Always filamentous)	98	Yes	Yes	Anaerolineaceae family. Chloroflexi phylum.
Ca *Amarolinea*	No (Always filamentous)	5	Yes	Yes	Anaerolineaceae family. Chloroflexi phylum.
Ca *Sarcinithrix*	No (Always filamentous)	13	Yes	Not Observed.	Amarolineaceae family. Chloroflexi phylum.
Tax ID 292628	Unknown	Unknown	Unknown	Likely	Anaerolineaceae family. Chloroflexi phylum.

Tax ID 292625	Unknown	Unknown	Unknown	Likely	Anaerolineaceae family. Chloroflexi phylum.
Tax ID 475963	Unknown	Unknown	Unknown	Likely	Caldilineales order. Chloroflexi phylum.
Tax ID 475964	Unknown	Unknown	Unknown	Likely	Caldilineales order. Chloroflexi phylum.
Tax ID 2303486	Unknown	Unknown	Unknown	Likely	Candidatus Amarolineaceae family, Chloroflexi phylum.
Tax ID 2303491	Unknown	Unknown	Unknown	Likely	Candidatus Amarolinea genus, Chloroflexi phylum.
Tax ID 200975	Unknown	Unknown	Unknown	Suspected	Chloroflexi phylum.

10.6G Nostocoida limicola (I and II) Morphotype Candidates and Correlations

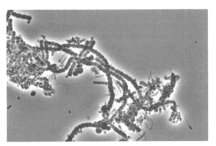

Figure: 10.30 Nostocoida I_II cropped from 1000x phase contrast

Genus or Lowest Read Obtained	Variable filament type y/n	Recognized # of species	MIDAS confirmed as filament capability y/n	RH-Aster Bio filament candidate y/n	Notes of Importance
Defluviicoccus	Yes	51	Yes	Yes	Alphaproteobacteria class. Proteobacteria phylum.
Tetrasphaera	Yes	33	Yes	Yes	Actinobacteria class. Actinobacteriota phylum.
Streptococcus	Yes	31	Yes	Yes	Bacilli class, Firmicutes phylum.
Lactococcus	Yes	12	Yes	Yes	Bacilli class. Firmicutes phylum.
Trichococcus	Yes	1	Yes	Yes-Variable	Bacilli class. Firmicutes phylum.
Paracoccus	Listed non-filamentous	95	No	Possibly	Alphaproteobacteria class. Proteobacteria phylum.

Romboutsia	Unknown	13	Unknown	Unknown	Peptostreptococcales-Tissierellales order. Firmicutes phylum.
Tax ID 112	Unknown	Unknown	Unknown	Possibly	Planctomycetales order. Planctomycetota phylum.
Tax ID 203682	Unknown	Unknown	Unknown	Potentially	Planctomycetota phylum.
Tax ID 2066434	Unknown	Unknown	Unknown	Potentially	Alphaproteobacteria class. Proteobacteria phylum.
Tax ID 1914233	Unknown	Unknown	Unknown	Potentially	Alphaproteobacteria class. Proteobacteria phylum.
Tax ID 468	Unknown	Unknown	Unknown	Potentially	Gammaproteobacteria class. Proteobacteria phylum.
Tax ID 1765324	Unknown	Unknown	Unknown	Potentially	Isosphaeraceae family. Planctomycetota phylum.
Tax ID 666507	Unknown	Unknown	Unknown	Potentially	Planctomycetota phylum.
Tax ID 666505	Unknown	Unknown	Unknown	Potentially	Planctomycetota phylum.

10.6H Type 0092 Morphotype Candidates and Correlations

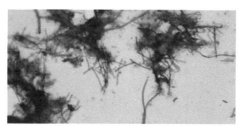

Figure: 10.31 type 0092 Neisser 1000x

Genus or Lowest Read Obtained	Variable filament type y/n	Recognized # of species	MIDAS confirmed as filament capability y/n	RH-Aster Bio filament candidate y/n	Notes of Importance
Ca *Promineofilum*	No (Always filamentous)	40	Yes	Yes	Anaerolineae class. Chloroflexi phylum.
Anaerolinea	No (Always filamentous)	98	Yes	Yes	Anaerolineae class. Chloroflexi phylum.

	No (Always filamentous)	5	Yes	Yes	Anaerolineae class. Chloroflexi phylum.
Ca *Amarolinea*	No (Always filamentous)	5	Yes	Yes	Anaerolineae class. Chloroflexi phylum.
Litorilinea	Unknown	5	Unknown	Yes	Anaerolineae class. Chloroflexi phylum.
Bellilinea	No (Always filamentous)	6	Yes	Yes	Anaerolineae class. Chloroflexi phylum.
Paracoccus	Listed non-filamentous	95	No	Possibly	Alphaproteobacteria class. Proteobacteria phylum.
Romboutsia	Unknown	13	Unknown	Unknown	Peptostreptococcales-Tissierellales order. Firmicutes phylum.
Tax ID 2303486	Unknown	Unknown	Unknown	Yes	Amarolineaceae family. Chloroflexi phylum.
Tax ID 292625	Unknown	Unknown	Unknown	Yes	Anaerolineae family. Chloroflexi phylum.
Tax ID 292628	Unknown	Unknown	Unknown	Yes	Anaerolineaceae family. Chloroflexi phylum.
Tax ID 200795	Unknown	Unknown	Unknown	Yes	Chloroflexi phylum.

10.6I Type 0581 Morphotype Candidates and Correlations

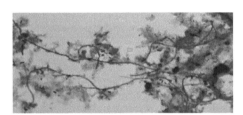

Figure: 10.32 type 0581 Gram stain 1000x

Genus or Lowest Read Obtained	Variable filament type y/n	Recognized # of species	MIDAS confirmed as filament capability y/n	RH-Aster Bio filament candidate y/n	Notes of Importance
Tax ID 292625	Unknown	Unknown	Unknown	Yes	Anaerolineae class. Chloroflexi phylum.
Tax ID 475964	Unknown	Unknown	Unknown	Yes	Caldilineaceae family. Chloroflexi phylum.
Tax ID 200795	Unknown	Unknown	Unknown	Yes	Chloroflexi phylum.

10.6J Type 0411 Morphotype Candidates and Correlations

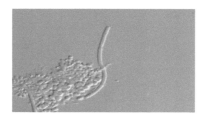

Figure: 10.33 type 0411 cropped 1000x DIC

Genus or Lowest Read Obtained	Variable filament type y/n	Recognized # of species	MIDAS confirmed as filament capability y/n	RH-Aster Bio filament candidate y/n	Notes of Importance
Runella	Unknown	31	Unknown	Yes	Bacteroidia class. Bacteroidota phylum.
Blastocatella	Yes	Unknown	Unknown	Yes	Blastocatellales order. Acidobacteriota phylum.
Tax ID 976	Unknown	Unknown	Unknown	Possibly	Bacteroidetes phylum.
Phaeodactylibacter	Unknown	52	Unknown	Possibly	Saprospiraceae family. Bacteroidota phylum.
Bacteriovorax	Unknown	34	Unknown	Possibly	Bdellovibrionota phylum.
Tax ID 49546	Unknown	Unknown	Unknown	Possibly	Flavobacteriaceae family. Bacteroidetes phylum.

10.6K Type 0211 Morphotype Candidates and Correlations

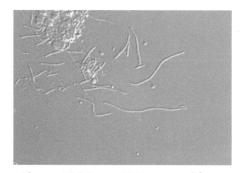

Figure: 10.34 type 0211 cropped from 1000x DIC

Genus or Lowest Read Obtained	Variable filament type y/n	Recognized # of species	MIDAS confirmed as filament capability y/n	RH-Aster Bio filament candidate y/n	Notes of Importance
Tax ID 84992	Unknown	Unknown	Unknown	Possibly	Acidimicrobiia class. Actinobacteria phylum.
Tax ID 89374	Unknown	Unknown	Unknown	Possibly	Saprospiraceae family. Bacteroidetes phylum.
Tax ID 57723	Unknown	Unknown	Unknown	Possibly	Acidobacteria phylum.

10.6L Microthrix Type Morphotype Candidates and Correlations

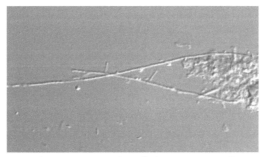

Figure: 10.35 Microthrix DIC cropped

Genus or Lowest Read Obtained	Variable filament type y/n	Recognized # of species	MIDAS confirmed as filament capability y/n	RH-Aster Bio filament candidate y/n	Notes of Importance
Ca Microthrix	No	6	Yes	Yes	Acidimicrobiia class. Actinobacteria phylum.
Iamia	Unknown	33	Unknown	Possibly	Acidimicrobiia class. Actinobacteria phylum.
Tax ID 2448023	Unknown	Unknown	Unknown	Possibly	Acidimicrobiia class. Actinobacteria phylum.
Tax ID 633392	Unknown	Unknown	Unknown	Possibly	Acidimicrobiia class. Actinobacteria phylum.
Tax ID 84992	Unknown	Unknown	Unknown	Possibly	Acidimicrobiia class. Actinobacteria phylum.

10.6M type 1863 Type Morphotype Candidates and Correlations

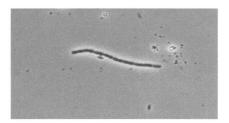

Figure: 10.36 type 1863 cropped

Genus or Lowest Read Obtained	Variable filament type y/n	Recognized # of species	MIDAS confirmed as filament capability y/n	RH-Aster Bio filament candidate y/n	Notes of Importance
Acinetobacter	Yes	90	Yes	Yes	Gammaproteobacteria class. Proteobacteria phylum.

10.6N Actinomycetes-Mycolata Morphotype Candidates and Correlations

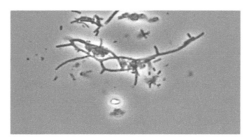

Figure: 10.37 Actinomycetes_Mycolata 1000x phase contrast

Genus or Lowest Read Obtained	Variable filament type y/n	Recognized # of species	MIDAS confirmed as filament capability y/n	RH-Aster Bio filament candidate y/n	Notes of Importance
Actinomyces	Yes	11	Yes	Yes	Actinobacteria class. Actinobacteriota phylum.
Dietzia	Yes	4	Yes	Yes	Actinobacteria class. Actinobacteriota phylum.

Stenotrophobacter	Unknown	23	Unknown	Yes	Blastocatellia class. Acidobacteriota phylum.
Tsukamurella	Unknown	Unknown	Unknown	Yes	Actinomycetia class. Actinobacteria; phylum. (NCBI classification/not in MIDAS).
Geothrix	Unknown	19	Unknown	Yes	Holophagae class. Acidobacteriota phylum.
Microbacterium	Unknown	55	Unknown	Likely	Actinobacteria class. Actinobacteriota phylum.
Propioniciclava	Unknown	50	Unknown	Yes	Actinobacteria class. Actinobacteriota phylum.
Gordonia	No (Always filamentous)	50	Yes	Yes	Actinobacteria class. Actinobacteriota phylum.
Skermania	No (Always filamentous)	2	Yes	Have not seen genus reads from Aster Bio	Actinobacteria class. Actinobacteriota phylum.
Mycobacterium	Yes	66	Yes	Yes	Actinobacteria class. Actinobacteriota phylum.
Tax ID 1760	Unknown	Unknown	Unknown	Possibly	Actinomycetia class. Actinobacteria phylum. (NCBI)
Tax ID 84992	Unknown	Unknown	Unknown	Likely	Acidimicrobiia class. Actinobacteria phylum. (NCBI)
Tax ID 588673	Unknown	Unknown	Unknown	Possibly	Thermoleophilia order. Actinobacteria phylum. (NCBI)
Tax ID 2448023	Unknown	Unknown	Unknown	Possibly	Acidimicrobiia class. Actinobacteria phylum. (NCBI)
Tax ID 1762	Unknown	Unknown	Unknown	Likely	Actinomycetia class. Actinobacteria phylum. (NCBI)
Tax ID 57723	Unknown	Unknown	Unknown	Possibly	Acidobacteria phylum. (NCBI)
Tax ID 31957	Unknown	Unknown	Unknown	Possibly	Actinomycetia class. Actinobacteria phylum. (NCBI)
Tax ID 85015	Unknown	Unknown	Unknown	Likely	Actinomycetia class. Actinobacteria phylum. (NCBI)
Tax ID 85018	Unknown	Unknown	Unknown	Likely	Actinomycetia class. Actinobacteria phylum. (NCBI)

Tax ID 85023	Unknown	Unknown	Unknown	Likely	Actinomycetia class. Actinobacteria phylum. (NCBI)
Paludibaculum	Unknown	Unknown	Unknown	Possibly	Acidobacteriia class. Acidobacteria phylum. (NCBI)
Tax ID 204432	Unknown	Unknown	Unknown	Possibly	Acidobacteriia class. Acidobacteria phylum. (NCBI)
Tax ID 633392	Unknown	Unknown	Unknown	Possibly	Acidobacteriia class. Acidobacteria phylum. (NCBI)

10.6O Filament Type 1851 Morphotype Candidates and Correlations

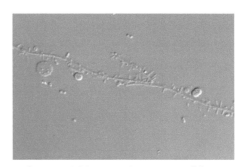

Figure: 10.38 type 1851 cropped from 1000x DIC

Genus or Lowest Read Obtained	Variable filament type y/n	Recognized # of species	MIDAS confirmed as filament capability y/n	RH-Aster Bio filament candidate y/n	Notes of Importance
Kouleothrix	No (always filamentous)	9	Yes	Yes	Chloroflexales order. Chloroflexi phylum.
Herpetosiphon	No (always filamentous)	1	Yes	Yes	Chloroflexales order. Chloroflexi phylum.
Anaerolineaceae UCG-001	Unknown	6	Unknown	Likely	Anaerolineales order. Chloroflexi phylum.
Ca *Saccharimonas*	Listed as non-filamentous	12	No	Yes	Saccharimonadales order. Patescibacteria phylum.
Roseiflexus	Not recognized in MIDAS	Unknown	Not recognized in MIDAS	Yes	Chloroflexales order. Chloroflexi phylum.
Tax ID 292625	Unknown	Unknown	Unknown	Yes	Anaerolineae class. Chloroflexi phylum.
Tax ID 475964	Unknown	Unknown	Unknown	Yes	Caldilineales order. Chloroflexi phylum.

Tax ID 292628	Unknown	Unknown	Unknown	Yes	Anaerolineales order. Chloroflexi phylum.
Tax ID 200795	Unknown	Unknown	Unknown	Yes	Unclassified Chloroflexi phylum.
Tax ID 32064	Unknown	Unknown	Unknown	Likely	Chloroflexales Order. Chloroflexi phylum.
Tax ID 1508635	Unknown	Unknown	Unknown	Likely	Roseiflexaceae family. Chloroflexi phylum.
Tax ID 119060	Unknown	Unknown	Unknown	Likely	Betaproteobacteria class. Proteobacteria phylum.

10.6P Filament Type 0041/0675 Morphotype Candidates and Correlations

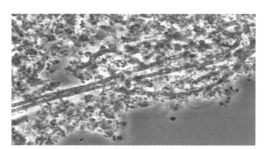

Figure: 10.39 type 0041_0675 cropped 1000x phase

Genus or Lowest Read Obtained	Variable filament type y/n	Recognized # of species	MIDAS confirmed as filament capability y/n	RH-Aster Bio filament candidate y/n	Notes of Importance
Roseiflexus	Not listed in MIDAS	Unknown	Not listed in MIDAS	Yes	Chloroflexales order. Chloroflexi phylum.
Ca *Saccharimonas*	Listed as non-filamentous	12	No	Yes	Saccharimonadales order. **Patescibacteria phylum.**
Herpetosiphon	No, always filamentous	1	Yes	Yes	Chloroflexales order. Chloroflexi phylum.
Tax ID 1508635	Unknown	Unknown	Unknown	Yes	Chloroflexales order. Chloroflexi phylum.
Tax ID 1382929	Unknown	Unknown	Unknown	Yes	Ardenticatenales order. Chloroflexi phylum.
Tax ID 1382930	Unknown	Unknown	Unknown	Yes	Ardenticatenales order. Chloroflexi phylum.
Tax ID 475964	Unknown	Unknown	Unknown	Yes	Caldilineaceae order. Chloroflexi phylum.
Tax ID 200795	Unknown	Unknown	Unknown	Yes	Chloroflexi phylum.

10.6Q Beggiatoa Morphotype Candidates and Correlations

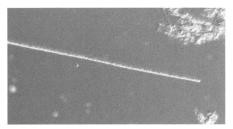

Figure: 10.40 Beggiatoa cropped from 200x DIC

Genus or Lowest Read Obtained	Variable filament type y/n	Recognized # of species	MIDAS confirmed as filament capability y/n	RH-Aster Bio filament candidate y/n	Notes of Importance
Beggiatoa	Unknown	7	Unknown in MIDAS	Not Observed	Gammaproteobacteria class. Proteobacteria phylum.
See Thiothrix/type 02N Unclassified Tax ID Reads	Unknown	Unknown	Unknown	Potentially	Various- likely Gammaproteobacteria class. Proteobacteria phylum apply.

10.7 Additional Candidates and Correlations for Non-Filamentous Morphotypes

10.7A Tetrads

Tetrads are a recognized grouping of 4 cells aggregated together. In wastewater treatment plants tetrads are often associated with organic acids and higher SRT values.

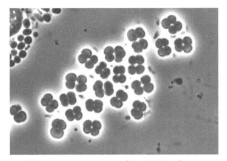

Figure: 10.41 tetrads 1000x phase

Genus or Lowest Read Obtained	Recognized # of species	MIDAS confirmed as tetrad capability y/n	RH-Aster Bio tetrad candidate y/n	RH filament candidate y/n	Notes of Importance
Tessaracoccus	19	Yes	Yes	No	Actinobacteria class. Actinobacteriota phylum.
Amaricoccus	55	Unknown	Yes	Yes (Nostocoida-like)	Alphaproteobacteria class. Proteobacteria phylum.
Rhodobacter	132	Unknown	Possibly	Not likely.	Alphaproteobacteria class. Proteobacteria phylum.
Paracoccus	95	Unknown	Likely	Possibly. (Nostocoida-like)	Alphaproteobacteria class. Proteobacteria phylum.
Defluviicoccus	51	Unknown	Yes	Yes- Confirmed Nostocoida morphology by MIDAS	Alphaproteobacteria class. Proteobacteria phylum.
Propioniciclava	50	Unknown	Possibly	Yes (Actinomycetes-Mycolata type)	Actinobacteria class. Actinobacteriota phylum.
Microbacterium	55	Unknown	Likely	Possibly Actinomycetes-Mycolata type	Actinobacteria class. Actinobacteriota phylum.
Micropruina	9	Yes	Yes	Possibly Actinomycetes-Mycolata type	Actinobacteria class. Actinobacteriota phylum.
Tax ID 84992	Unknown	Unknown	Possibly	Possibly Actinomycetes-Mycolata type	Acidimicrobiia class. Actinobacteria phylum (NCBI)
Tax ID 1762	Unknown	Unknown	Possibly	Possibly Actinomycetes-Mycolata type	Actinomycetia class. Actinobacteria phylum (NCBI)
Micromonospora	Unknown	Genus not recognized by MIDAS	Possibly	Unknown	NCBI- Actinomycetia class. Actinobacteria phylum.
Tax ID 1760	Unknown	Unknown	Possibly	Possibly Actinomycetes-Mycolata type	NCBI- Actinomycetia class. Actinobacteria phylum.
Tax ID 85023	Unknown	Unknown	Possibly	Possibly Actinomycetes-Mycolata type	NCBI- Actinomycetia class. Actinobacteria phylum.
Tax ID 666507	Unknown	Unknown	Possibly	Possibly Nostocoida-like	Planctomycetes phylum (NCBI).

10.7B Zoogloea Morphotype Candidates and Correlations

Zoogloea bacteria morphotypes are recognized as single clusters of individual cells that contain a thick polysaccharide (slime) capsule.

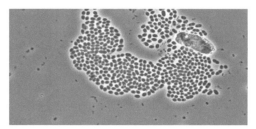

Figure: 10.42 zoogloea cropped from 1000x phase contrast

Genus or Lowest Read Obtained	Recognized # of species	RH-Aster Bio Zoogloea morphotype candidate y/n	Notes of Importance
Thauera	21	Yes	Gammaproteobacteria class. Proteobacteria phylum.
Zoogloea	29	Yes	Gammaproteobacteria class. Proteobacteria phylum.
Rhodobacter	132	Maybe	Alphaproteobacteria class. Proteobacteria phylum.
Rhodoferax	55	Possibly	Gammaproteobacteria class. Proteobacteria phylum.
Uliginosibacterium	16	Possibly	Gammaproteobacteria class. Proteobacteria phylum.
Tax ID 31989	Unknown	Possibly	Alphaproteobacteria class. Proteobacteria phylum.
Tax ID 1775411	Unknown	Possibly	Gammaproteobacteria class. Proteobacteria phylum.
Tax ID 75787	Unknown	Possibly	Betaproteobacteria class. Proteobacteria phylum.

10.7C Spirilla, Flexibacter, Spirochaetes, and Microscrilla

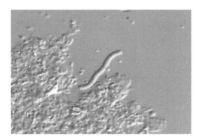

Figure: 10.43 spillum DIC cropped from 1000x

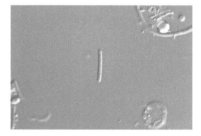

Figure: 10.44 Flexibacter 1000x DIC cropped

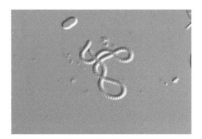

Figure: 10.45 Spirochaetes cropped from 1000x DIC

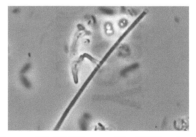

Figure: 10.46 Microscrilla 1000x phase contrast cropped

The above morphotypes are small motile microbes associated with elevated organic acid concentrations if present at high abundance.

AT THE PRESENT TIME, POTENTIAL DNA CORRELATIONS APPEAR TOO NUMEROUS TO ATTEMPT TO ACCOUNT FOR.

Picture Library

Sphaerotilus filament morphotype (low DO)

Sphaerotilus	Commonly has false branching	1.2-2.6 µm diaeer	Yes/ Septa Visible	No/Sulfur Granules	Sausage Shaped. 1.6 x 2.5	Yes/ Sheath

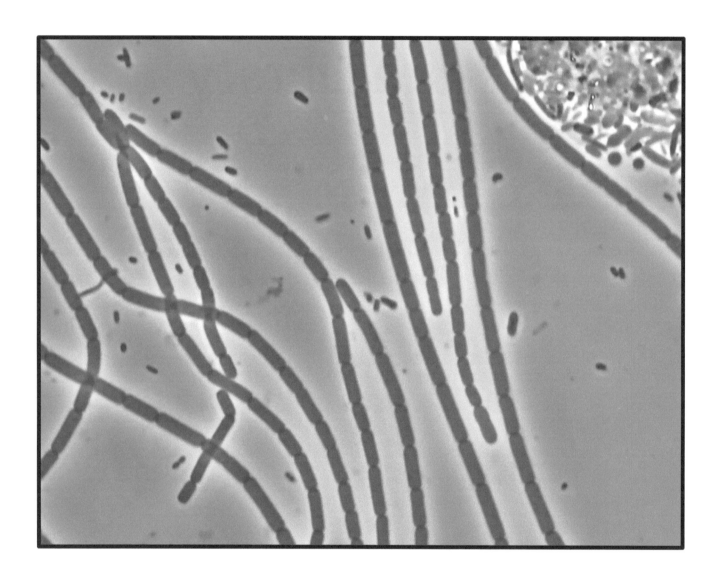

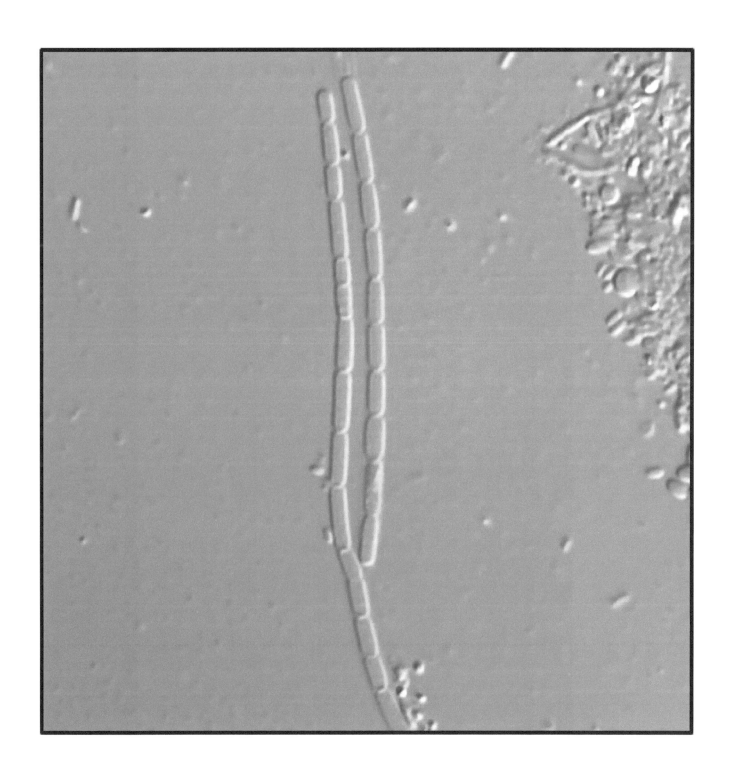

Type 1701 filament morphotype (low DO)

Type 1701	Thinner filament with sausage shaped cells (sometimes cells are hard to see). Occasionally has attached growth	0.8- 1.0 µm diameter	Yes- Usually/but not always visible septa	No sulfur granules	Sausage shaped. 1.0 x 1.5	Yes/Sheath

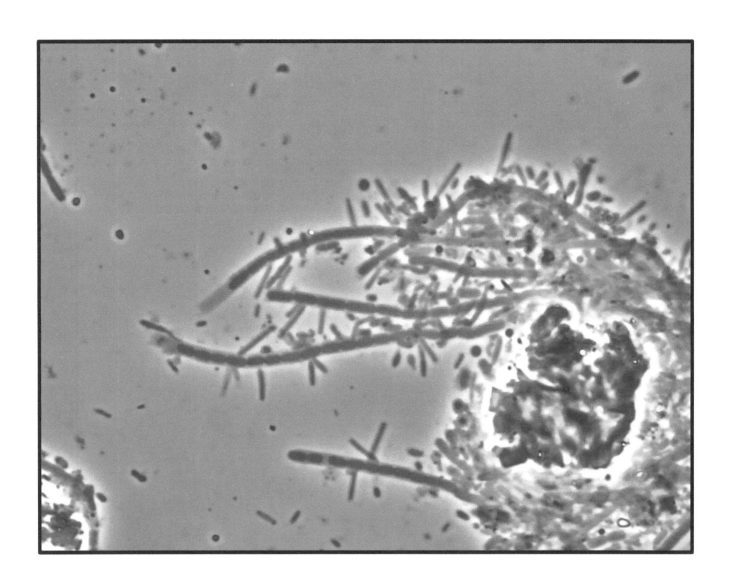

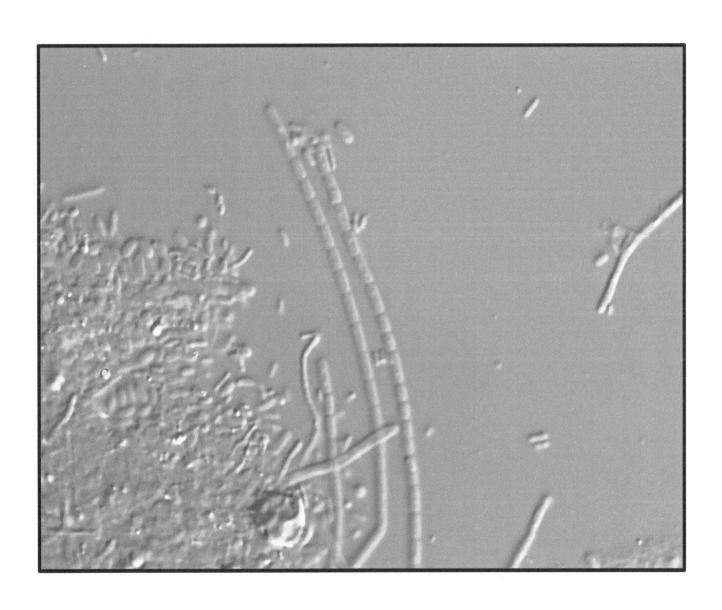

Haliscomenobacter filament morphotype (variable potential causes)

| Haliscomenobacter | 0.5 um diameter (skinny). Often "pins in a pin cushion". Sheath often difficult to see | 0.5 μm diameter | No- Usually cannot observed Septa | No/ Sulfur Granules | Usually can't see individual cells. Occasionally small sausage shaped cells are visible | Yes/ Sheath |

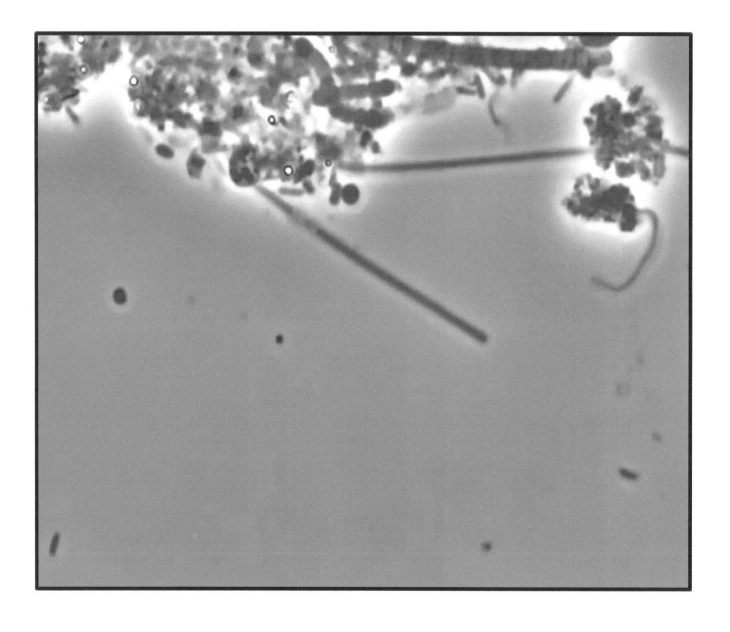

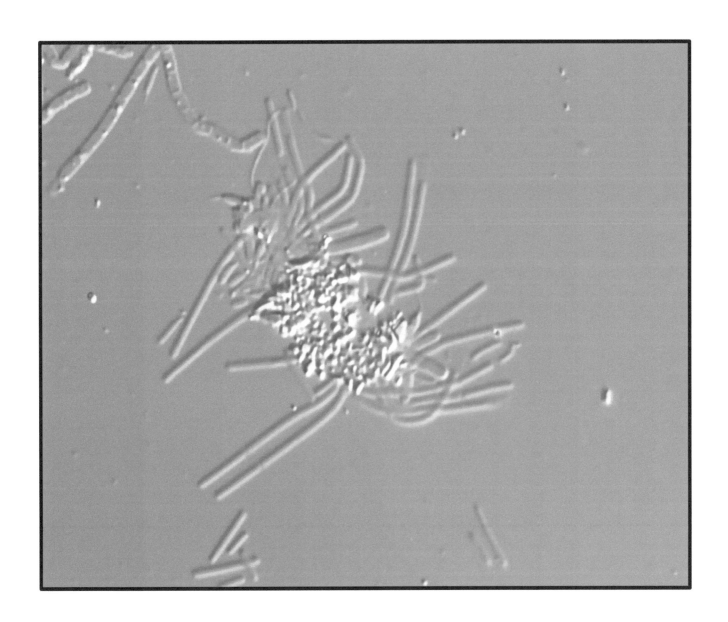

Type 021N filament morphotype (organic acids/sulfide)

Type 021N	Large filament that typically extends from the flocs or bridges flocs together. Irregular cell shape	1.6-2.5 μm Diameter	Yes/ Septa Visible	Yes/ Potential for Sulfur Granules	Barrels, rectangles, discoid. 1.6 X 2.5 μm	No/ Sheath

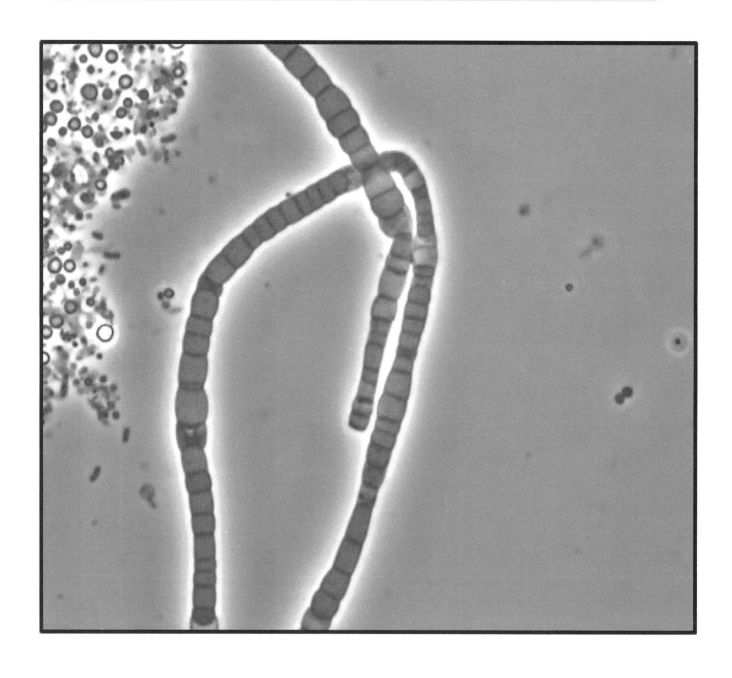

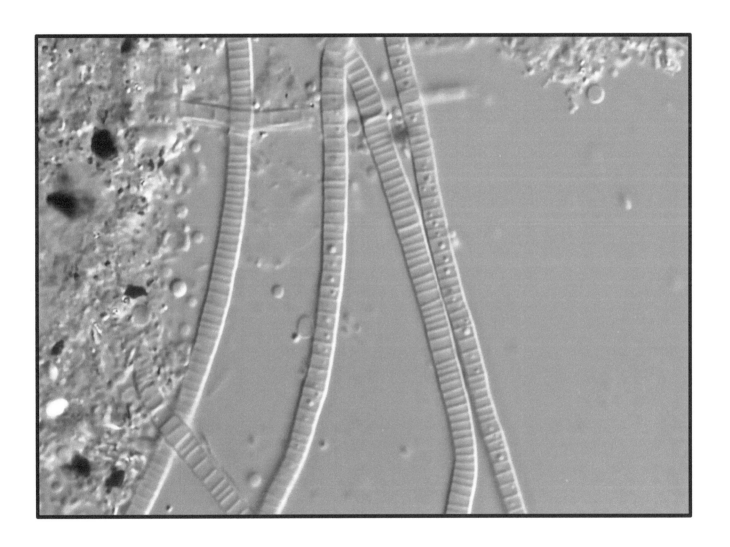

Thiothrix filament morphotype (organic acids/sulfide)

Thiothrix	Rectangular cell shape. Typically extends from flocs	0.8- 2.8 µm Diameter	Yes/ Septa Visible	Yes/ Potential for Sulfur Granules	Rectangles. 0.8-1.4 x 1.0-3.0 µm	Yes/ Sheath

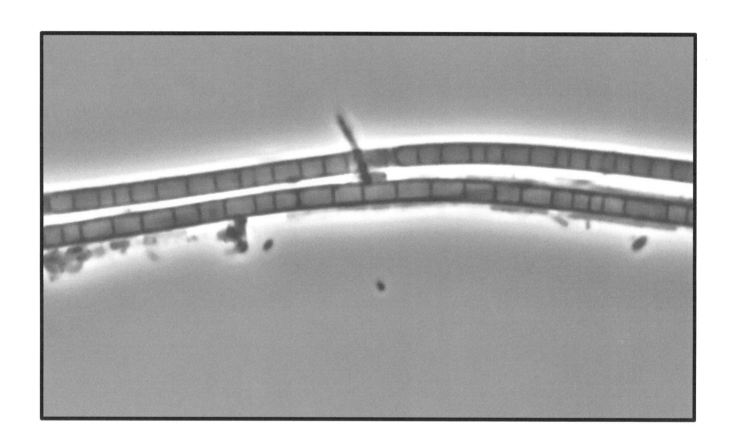

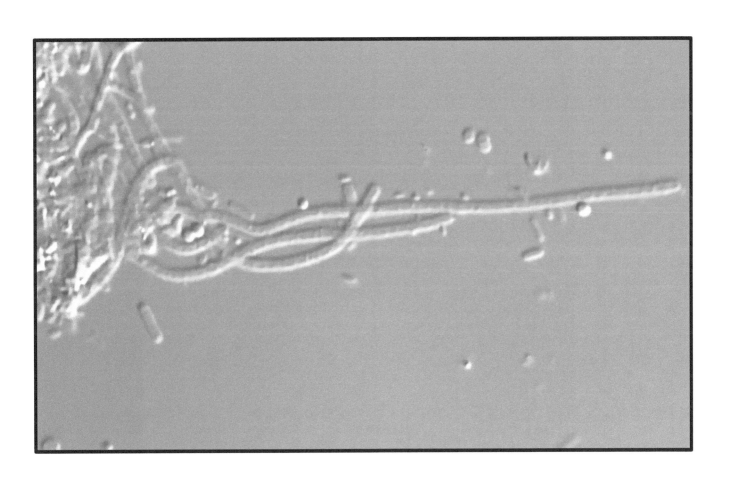

169

Type 0914/0803 filament morphotype (organic acids/sulfide)

Type 0914/0803	Occasionally has square sulfur granules	1.0-1.2 μm Diameter	Yes/ Septa Usually Visible	Yes/ Potential for Sulfur Granules	Square. 1.0 x 1.0 μm	Yes/ Sheath

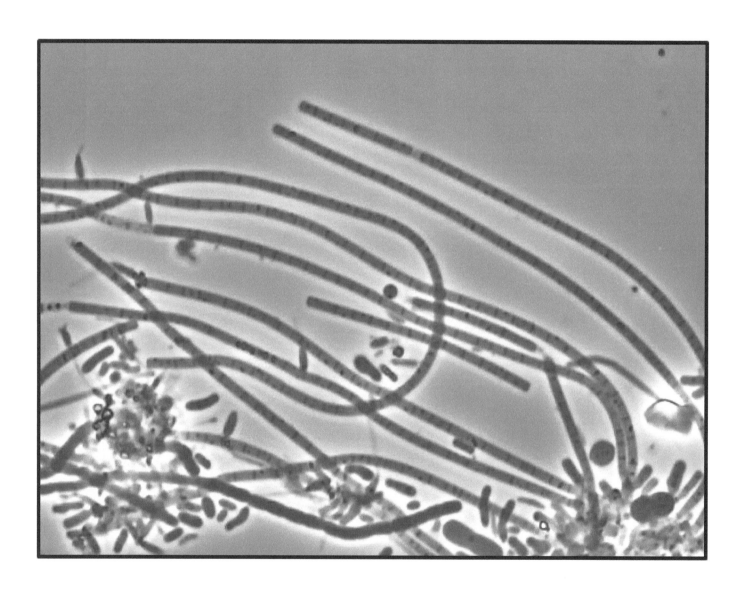

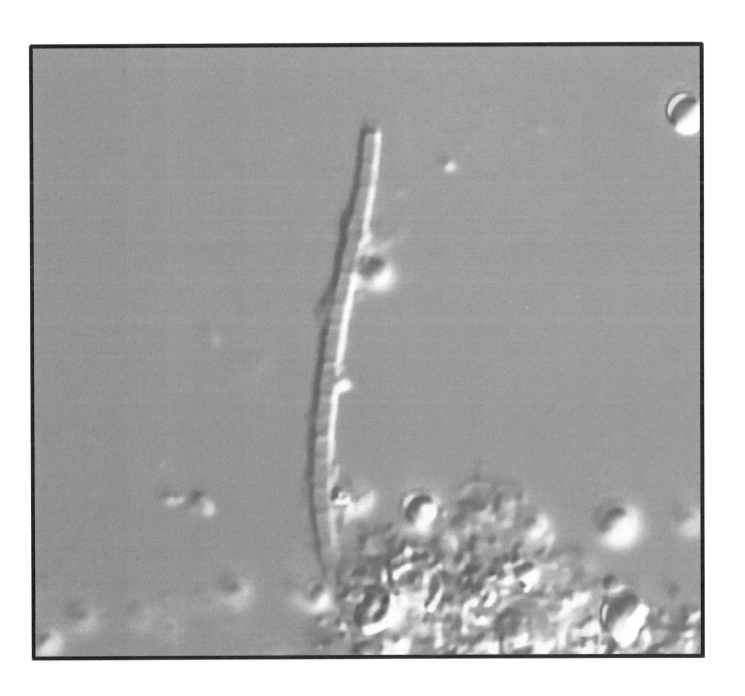

171

Beggiatoa filament morphotypes (organic acids/sulfide)

Beggiatoa	Typically motile and usually contains either sulfur granules or PHB granules	2.0- 4.0 µm Diameter	Sometimes can see septa.	Yes/ Potential for Sulfur Granules	Rectangles. 2.0-4.0 x 6.0 -8.0 µm	Sheath/ No

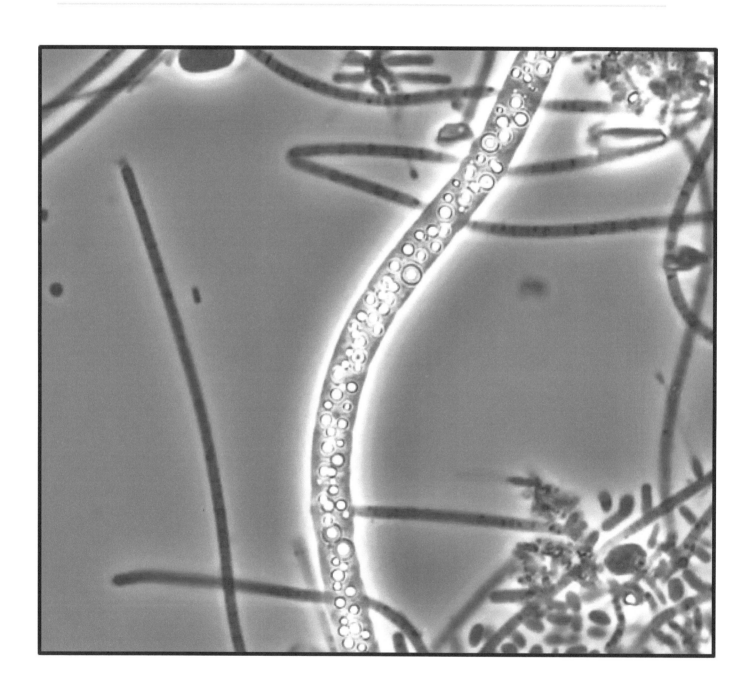

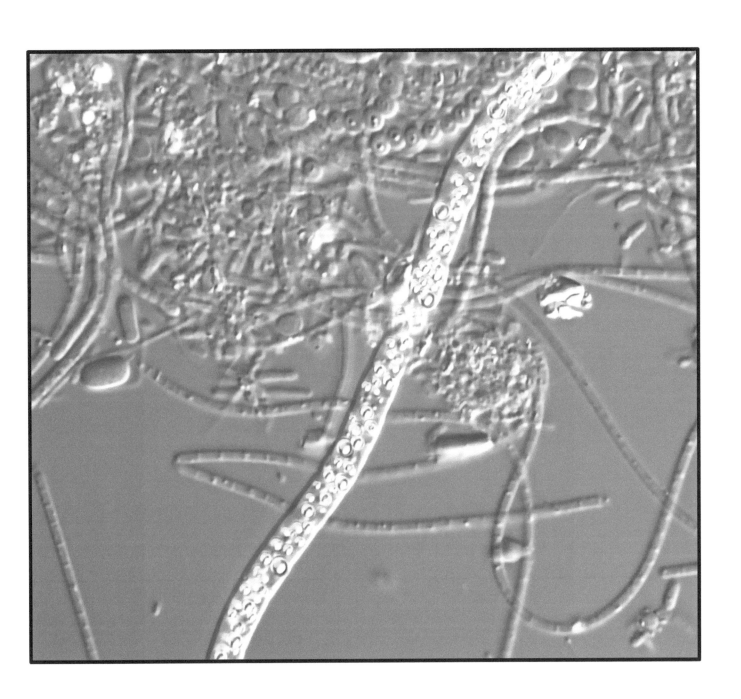

Nostocoida limicola (I and II) filament morphotype (organic acids)

Nostocoida limicola I and II	"Hockey pucks".	0.8-2.0 µm Diameter	Yes/ Septa Visible	No/ Sulfur Granules	Discs, ovals. 0.8 x 1.0-1.5 µm	No/ Sheath

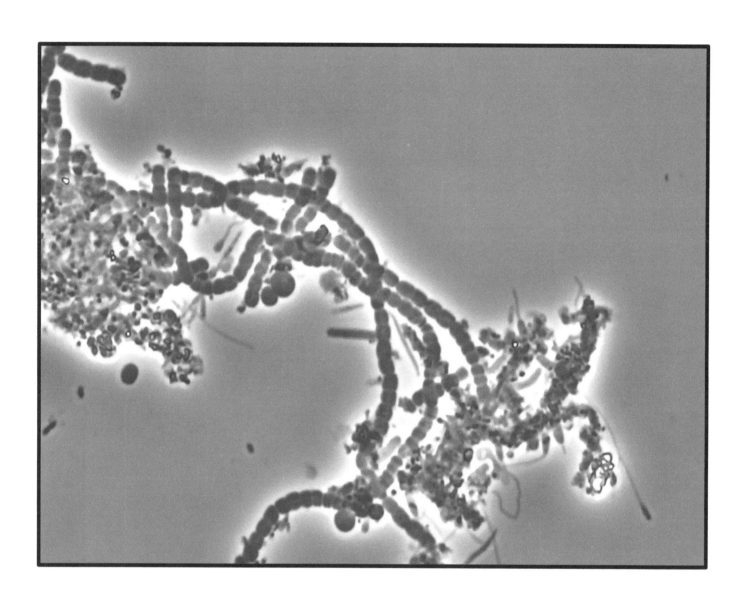

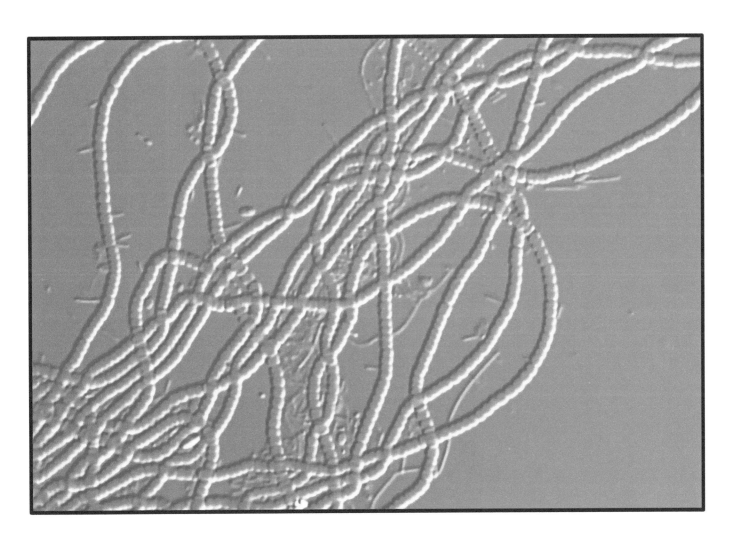

Nostocoida limicola III filament morphotype (organic acids)

Nostocoida limicola III	Individual discoid cells	1.7-2.5 μm Diameter	Yes/ Septa Visible	No/ Sulfur Granules	Discs, Ovals 2.0 x 1.5 μm	No/ Sheath

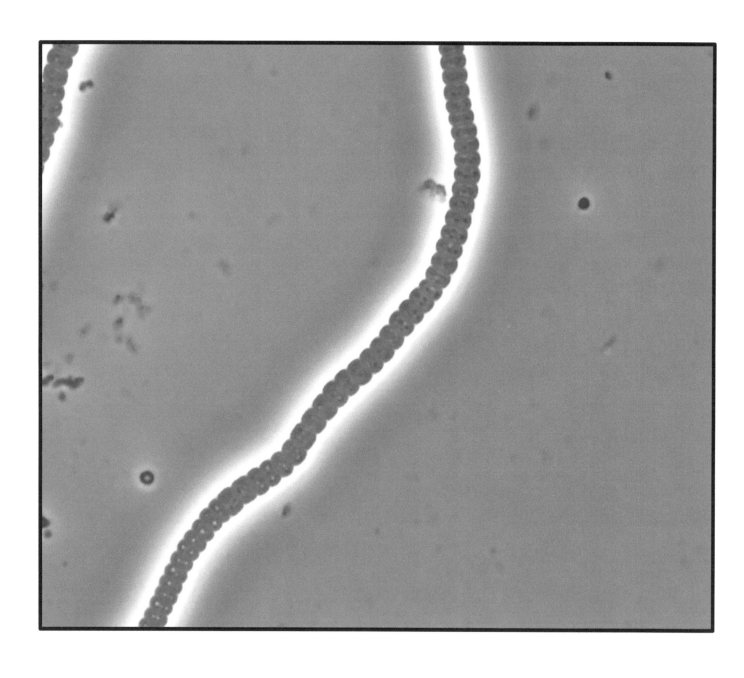

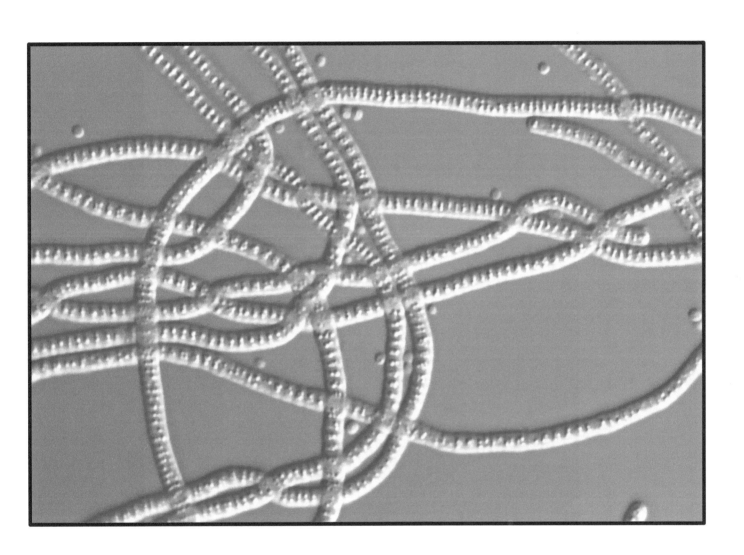

Filament type 0411 morphotype (organic acids)

Type 0411	"Elongated rods/ long sausage links"	0.8-1.2 µm Diameter	Yes/ Septa Visible	No/ Sulfur Granules	Sausage, Rods. 0.8-1.2 x 2.0-5.0 µm	No/ Sheath

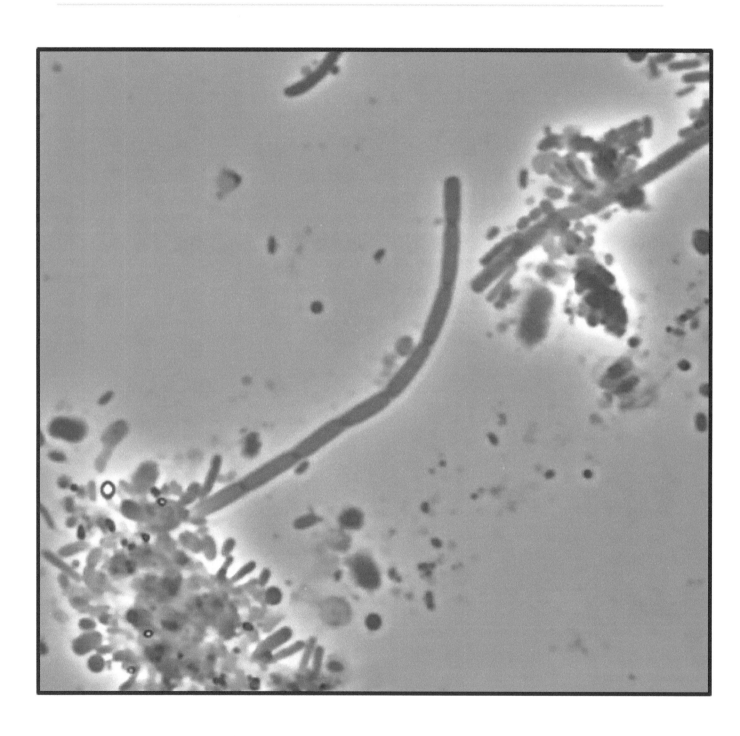

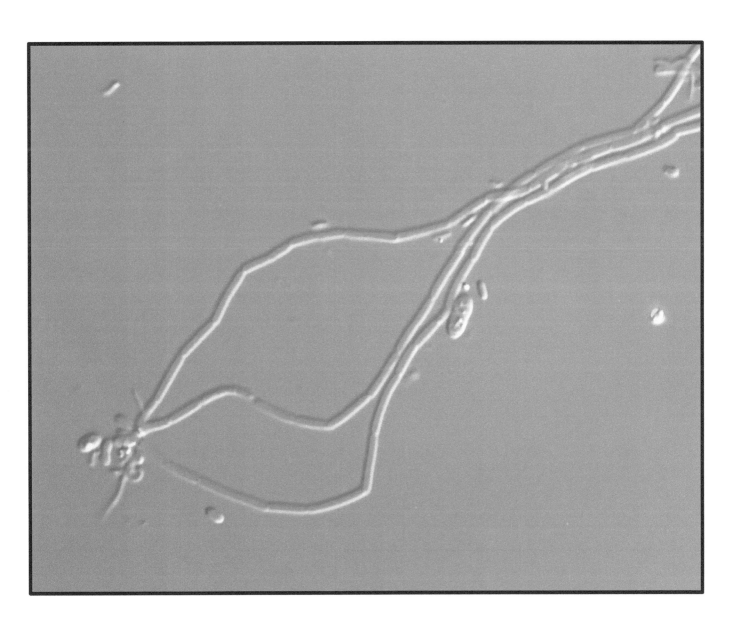

Filament type 0961 (organic acids)

Type 0961	Transparent/ "lighter" appearance.	1.0-1.4 µm Diameter	Yes/ Septa Visible	No/ Sulfur Granules	Rectangles. 1.0-1.4 x 2.0-4.0 µm	No (not a true sheath)

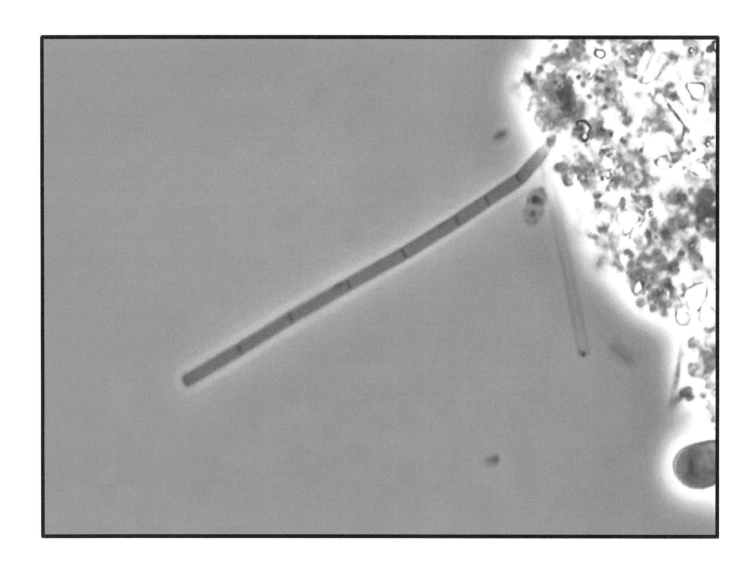

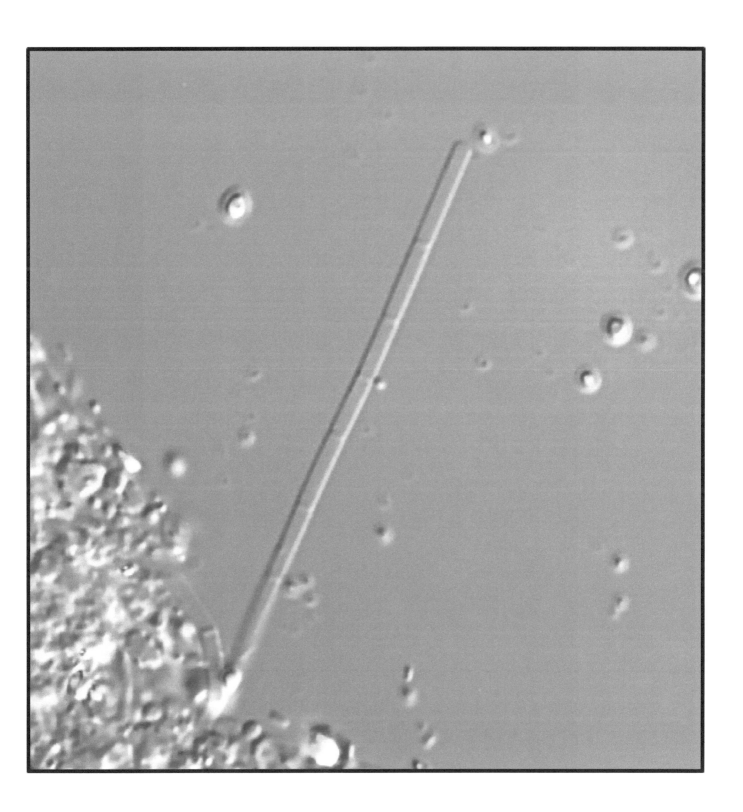

Filament type 0092 (organic acids)

Type 0092	Neisser positive. Need Neisser stain to ID. Often difficult to see at phase contrast	0.6-1.2 μm Diameter	Yes- Sometimes but not always/ Septa Visible	No/ Sulfur Granules	Rectangles. 0.8-1.0 x 1.0 μm (Common to not see individual cells)	Sheath/ Variable

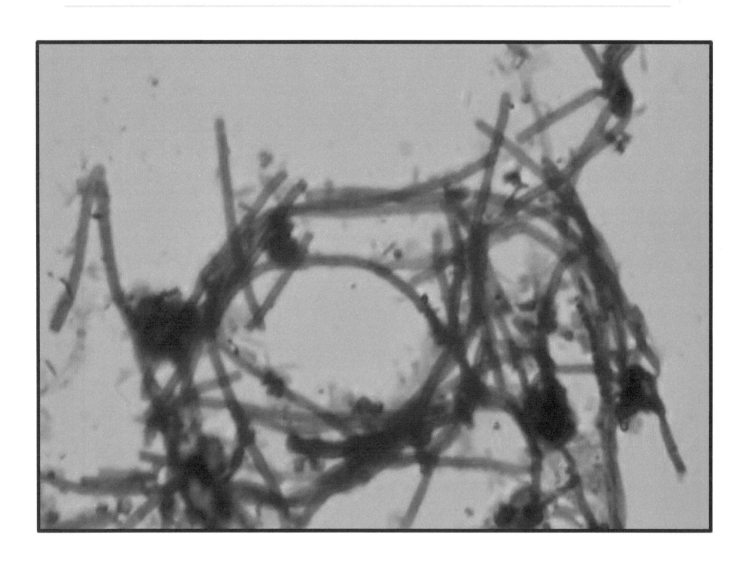

Filament Type 1863 morphotype (fats, oils, grease)

Type 1863	Usually dispersed. "Chain of cells" appearance	0.8-1.0 μm Diameter	Yes/ Septa Visible	No/ Sulfur Granules	Oval rods. 0.8-1.0 x 1.0-1.5 μm	No/ Sheath

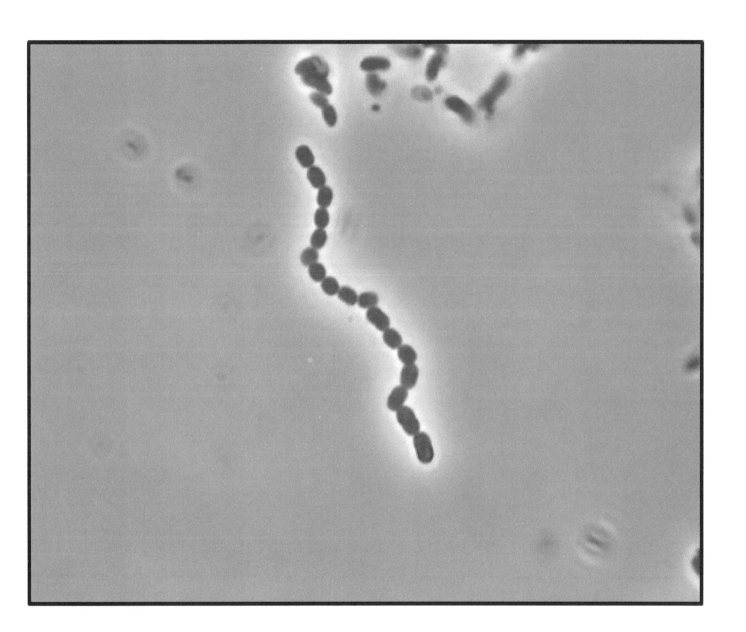

Filament type 0041/0675 morphotype (high SRT)

Type 0041/0675	"Grainy" appearance. Often has attached growth	1.0-2.2 μm Diameter	Yes/ Septa Visible	No/ Sulfur Granules	Squares. 1.0-2.0 x 2.0-3.0 μm	Yes/ Sheath

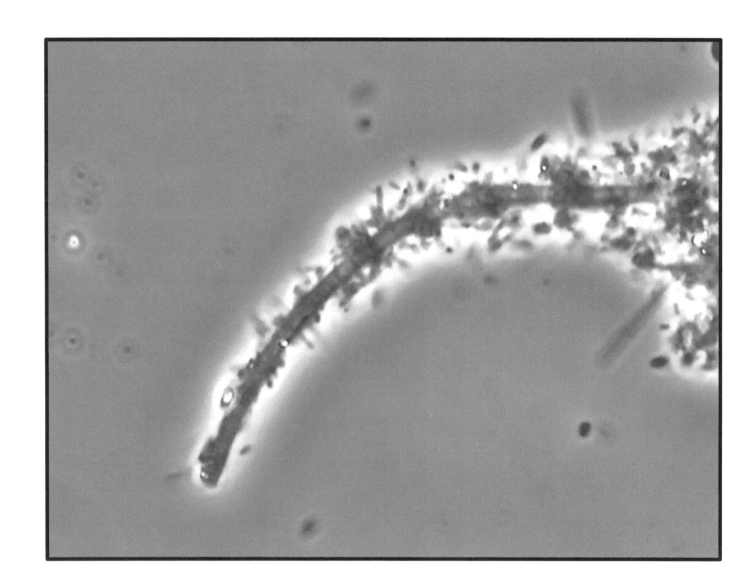

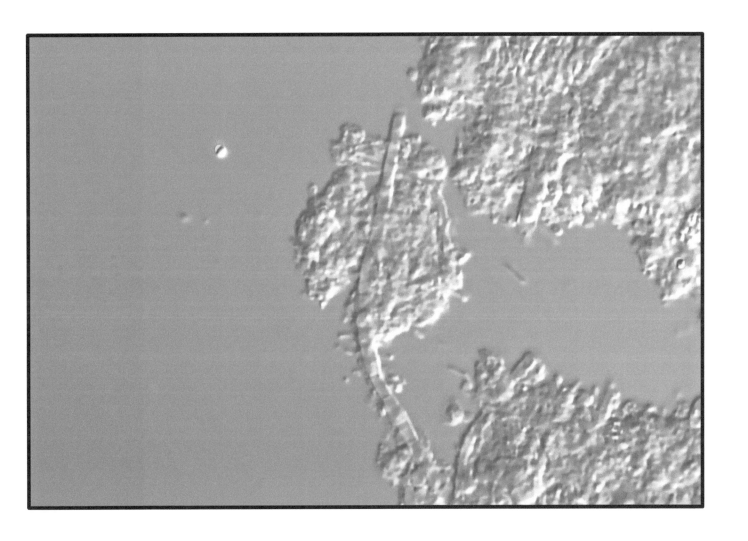

Type 1851 filament morphotype (high SRT)

Type 1851	Often forms "bundles/twisted ropes". Often has attached growth	0.8 μm- 1 μm Diameter	Often difficult to view septa.	No/ Sulfur Granules	Rectangles. Generally 0.8 x 1.4 μm ballpark	Yes/ Sheath

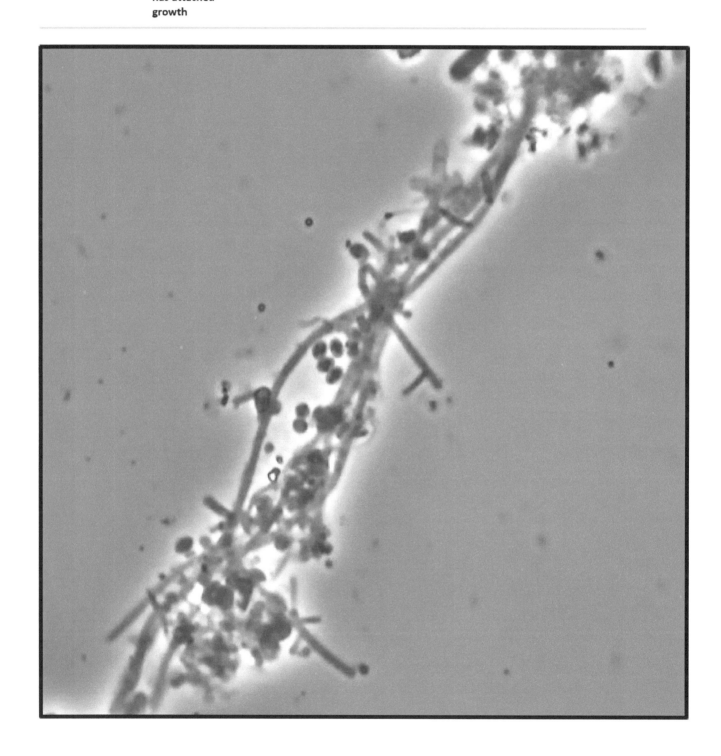

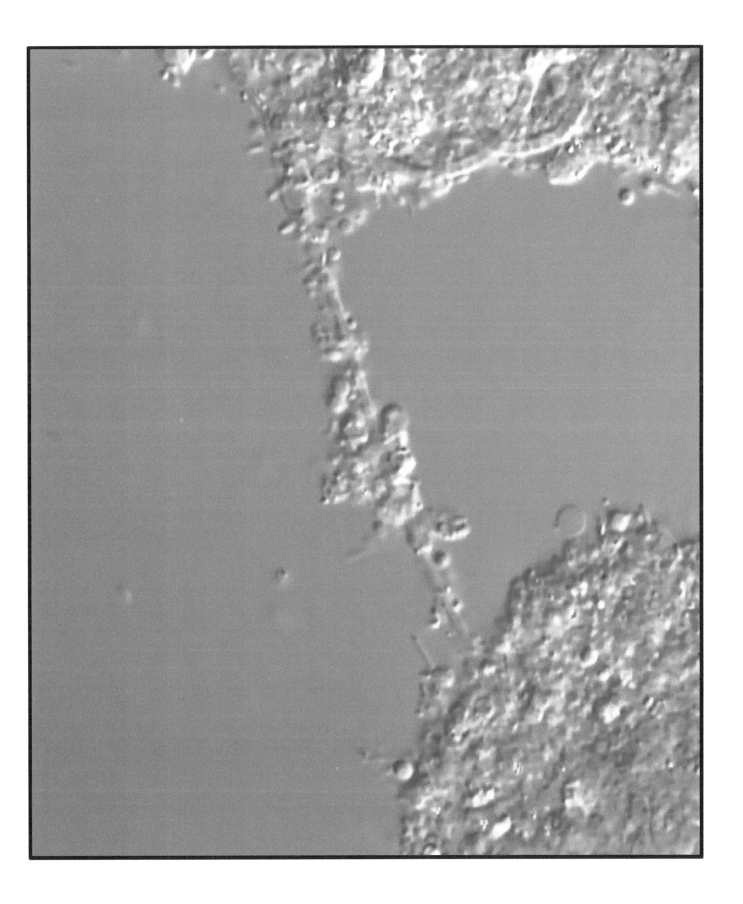

187

Microthrix filament morphotype (oleic acid/fats, oils, grease)

Microthrix	Gram positive. Often has Neisser positive granules. Typically "coiled"	0.5-0.8µm Diameter	Very rarely see septa	No/ Sulfur Granules	-------------------- Typically can't see individual cells	No/ Sheath

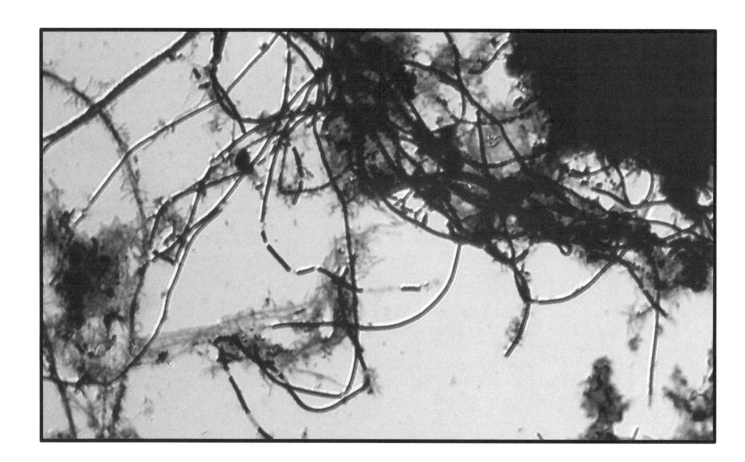

Actinomycetes-Mycolata (fats, oils, grease and/or organic acids/ variable other causes)

Actinomycetes-Mycolata	"True branching". Almost all species in wastewater stain gram positive when healthy	0.8-1.2µm Diameter	Yes- most species Septa is visible	No/ Sulfur Granules	Variable. 1.0 x 1.0- 2.0 µm	No/ Sheath

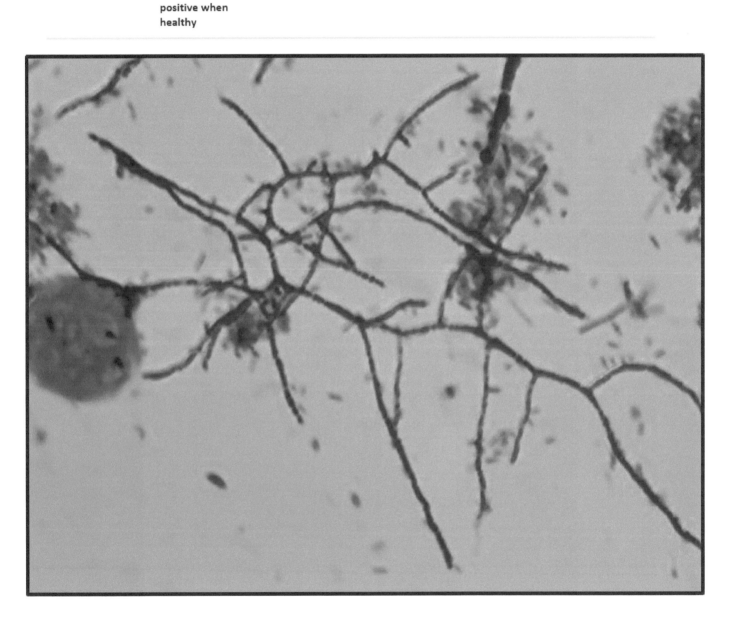

Filament type 0211 morphotype (organic acids)

Type 0211	Grows dispersed. "Thin and crooked"	0.3-0.4 μm Diameter	Yes/ Septa usually visible	No/ Sulfur Granules	Oval rods. 0.4 x 0.6 μm	No/ Sheath

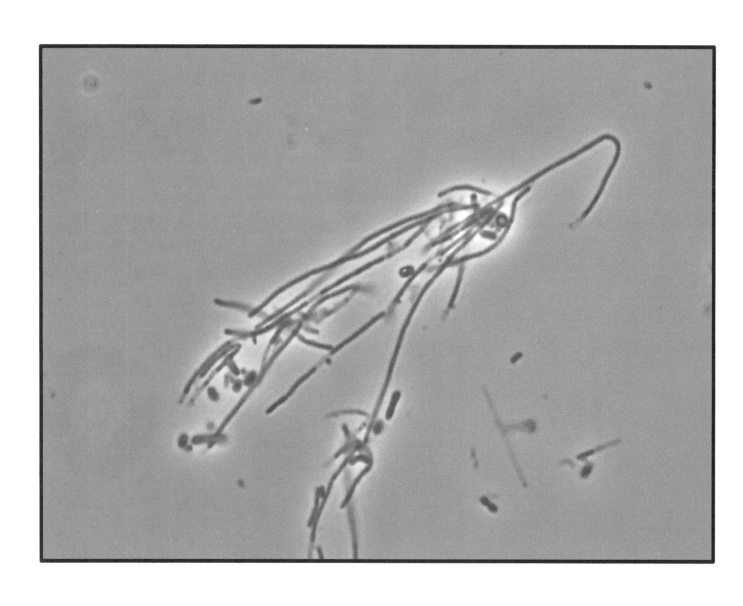

Filament type 0581 (organic acids)

Type 0581	Looks like *Microthrix* but gram positive	0.5-0.8 μm Diameter	No/ Septa Usually not Visible	No/ Sulfur Granules	_____	No/ Sheath

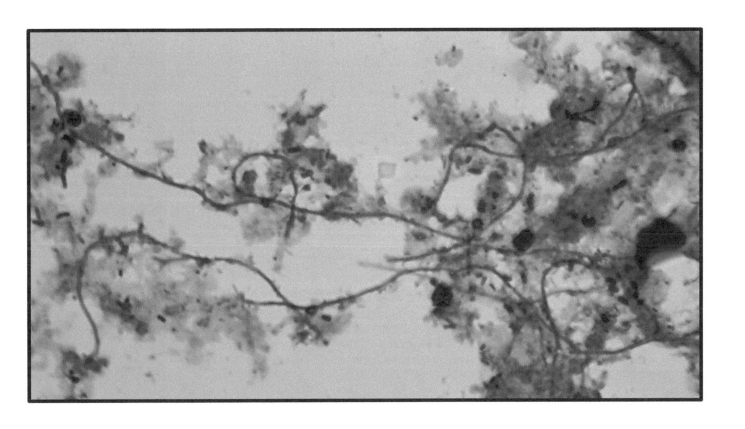

Fungi morphotype (low pH)

Fungi	Very Large/True branching	5.0-10.0 μm Diameter	Sometimes/ Septa Visible	No Sulfur Granules	Variable/ Cell Shape/Size	No Sheath (but does often have thick cellulose cell wall)

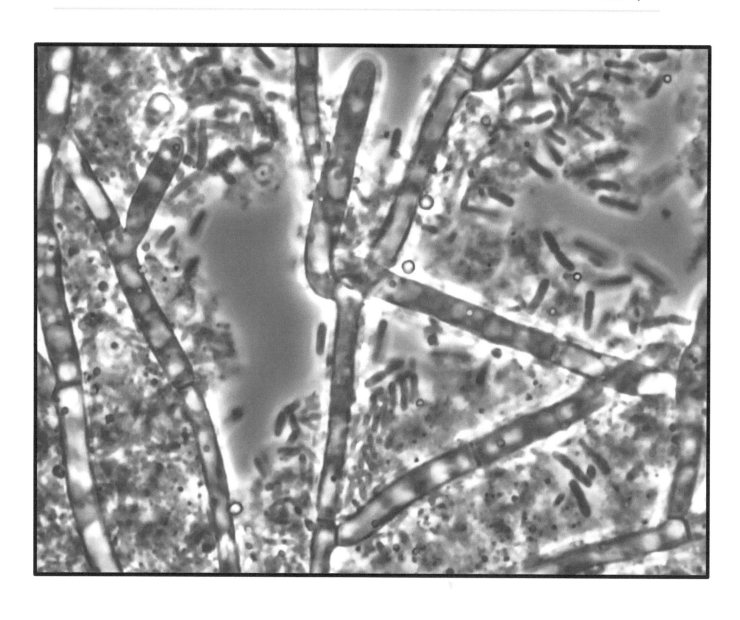

References

Absorption vs Adsorption. (n.d.). Diffen. Retrieved December 21, 2021, from https://www.diffen.com/difference/Absorption_vs_Adsorption

Amasci Creative Limited. (2018a, January 16). What are membrane bioreactors? The MBR Site. Retrieved December 23, 2021, from https://www.thembrsite.com/membrane-bioreactor-basics/what-are-mbrs/

Amasci Creative Limited. (2018b, March 20). O&M – MBR fouling, clogging and cleaning. The MBR Site. https://www.thembrsite.com/operation-maintenance/mbr-fouling-clogging-cleaning/

American Society for Microbiology. (n.d.). Nomenclature. ASM Journals. Retrieved December 30, 2021, from https://journals.asm.org/nomenclature

Anbu, S., Gopinath, S. C. B., Chaulagain, B. P., Lakshmipriya, T. (2017.) Microbial enzymes and their applications in industry and medicine. BioMed Research International, 2017. https://doi.org/10.1155/2017/2195808

Balvočiūtė, M., & Huson, D. H. (2017). SILVA, RDP, Greengenes, NCBI and OTT — how do these taxonomies compare? BMC Genomics, 18(S2). https://doi.org/10.1186/s12864-017-3501-4

Berg, J. M., Tymoczko, J. L., Stryer, L. (2002.) Biochemistry. 5th edition. New York: W. H. Freeman. Cooke, R. (n.d.). Lesson 8: Nitrification and Denitrification. ENV 149 Wastewater Treatment Plant Operation. Retrieved December 10, 2021, from https://water.mecc.edu/courses/ENV149_/lesson8_print.htm

Bitton, G. (2005). The Biology of Activated Sludge. In Wastewater Microbiology (Third Edition, pp. 238–240). Wiley.

Blackwood, C. B., Oaks, A., & Buyer, J. S. (2005). Phylum- and Class-Specific PCR Primers for General Microbial Community Analysis. Applied and Environmental Microbiology, 71(10), 6193–6198. https://doi.org/10.1128/aem.71.10.6193-6198.2005

Bradford, A., & Weisberger, M. (2021, November 12). Facts about tardigrades. Livescience.Com. https://www.livescience.com/57985-tardigrade-facts.html

Bukin, Y. S., Galachyants, Y. P., Morozov, I. V., Bukin, S. V., Zakharenko, A. S., & Zemskaya, T. I. (2019). The effect of 16S rRNA region choice on bacterial community metabarcoding results. Scientific Data, 6(1). https://doi.org/10.1038/sdata.2019.7

Calculating the Hydraulic Retention Time. (2021). Lenntech. https://www.lenntech.com/wwtp/calculate-hrt.html

Choosing A Microscope Camera - What To Look For. (n.d.). Microscope Central. https://microscopecentral.com/pages/choosing-a-microscope-camera-what-to-look-for

Doroghazi, J. R., & Metcalf, W. W. (2013). Comparative genomics of actinomycetes with a focus on natural product biosynthetic genes. BMC Genomics, 14(1), 611. https://doi.org/10.1186/1471-2164-14-611

Dueholm, M.S., Nierychlo, M., Andersen, K.S., Rudkjøbing, V., Knudsen, S., the MiDAS Global Consortium, Albertsen, M., Nielsen, P.H. 2021. MiDAS 4: A global catalogue of full-length 16S rRNA gene sequences and taxonomy for studies of bacterial communities in wastewater treatment plants. https://doi.org/10.1101/2021.07.06.451231.

Encyclopedia Britannica. (n.d.-a). gastrotrich|invertebrate. Retrieved December 16, 2021, from https://www.britannica.com/animal/gastrotrich

Encyclopedia Britannica. (n.d.-b). nematode | Definition, Description, Diseases, & Facts. Retrieved December 16, 2021, from https://www.britannica.com/animal/nematode

Encyclopedia Britannica. (n.d.-c). tardigrade | Facts & Lifespan. Retrieved December 16, 2021, from https://www.britannica.com/animal/tardigrade

Evans, M., and Sober, G. How alkalinity affects nitrification. Emerging Issues Article. (n.d.) Retrieved November 22, 2021, from https://www.cwea.org/news/how-alkalinity-affects-nitrification/.

Evoqua Water Technologies. (2021). Tertiary Wastewater Filtration. Evoqua. Retrieved December 21, 2021, from https://www.evoqua.com/en/markets/applications/tertiary-wastewater-filtration/

Frankel, T. (2019, November 29). What Is MBBR Wastewater Treatment & How Does It Work? SSI: Smart Ideas for Water. Retrieved December 21, 2021, from https://www.ssiaeration.com/what-is-mbbr-how-does-it-work/

Fuller, R. (2016, December 18). ORP. The Wastewater Blog. Retrieved December 21, 2021, from https://www.thewastewaterblog.com/single-post/2016/12/18/orp

Garg, M. (2016, September 16). Bacterial Taxonomy: Meaning, Importance and Levels. Biology Discussion. https://www.biologydiscussion.com/bacteria/bacterial-taxonomy/bacterial-taxonomy-meaning-importance-and-levels/54679

Gray, D. M., de Lange, V. P., Chien, M. H., Esquer, M. A., & Shao, Y. (2010). Investigating the Fundamental Basis for Selectors to Improve Activated Sludge Settling. Water Environment Research, 82(6), 541–555. https://doi.org/10.2175/106143009x12529484815791

Hennessy, R. (2020, November 16). Bug of the Month: Zoogloea, the Glue of Floc Formation. Treatment Plant Operator. Retrieved January 17, 2022, from https://www.tpomag.com/online_exclusives/2020/11/bug-of-the-month-zoogloea-the-glue-of-floc-formation

Hill, P. (2016, August 19). Lagoon Algae Prevention And Control: Strategies And Methods. Triplepoint Environmental. https://lagoons.com/blog/algae/lagoon-algae-prevention/

How To Center For Koehler Illumination. (n.d.). Microscope Central. Retrieved December 14, 2021, from https://microscopecentral.com/pages/how-to-center-for-koehler-illumination

How To Center For Phase Contrast. (n.d.). Microscope Central. Retrieved December 14, 2021, from https://microscopecentral.com/pages/how-to-center-for-phase-contrast

Iorhemen, O., Hamza, R., & Tay, J. (2016). Membrane Bioreactor (MBR) Technology for Wastewater Treatment and Reclamation: Membrane Fouling. Membranes, 6(2), 33. https://doi.org/10.3390/membranes6020033

Jenkins, D., Richard, M. G., & Dagger, G. T. (2004). Manual on the Causes and Control of Activated Sludge Bulking, Foaming, and Other Solids Separation Problems (3rd ed.). CRC Press.

Johnson, J. S., Spakowicz, D. J., Hong, B. Y., Petersen, L. M., Demkowicz, P., Chen, L., Leopold, S. R., Hanson, B. M., Agresta, H. O., Gerstein, M., Sodergren, E., & Weinstock, G. M. (2019). Evaluation of 16S rRNA gene sequencing for species and strain-level microbiome analysis. Nature Communications, 10(1). https://doi.org/10.1038/s41467-019-13036-1

Judd, S. (2012). The MBR Book (2nd ed.). Elsevier Science.

Kelly, D. J., Hughes, N. J., & Poole, R. K. (2001). Chapter 10: Microaerobic Physiology: Aerobic Respiration, Anaerobic Respiration, and Carbon Dioxide Metabolism. In Helicobacter pylori: Physiology and Genetics. (p. NA). ASM Press. https://www.ncbi.nlm.nih.gov/books/NBK2411/

Khodabakhshi, N., Asadollahfardi, G., & Shahriarinia, E. (2015). Removal of foaming from industrial wastewater treatment plants. Water Practice and Technology, 10(3), 415–423. https://doi.org/10.2166/wpt.2015.031

Kosakyan, A., Lara, E. (2019). Using Testate Amoebae Communities to Evaluate Environmental Stress: A Molecular Biology Perspective. Reference Module in Earth Systems and Environmental Sciences (p. na). https://doi.org/10.1016/B978-0-12-409548-9.11589-1

Kralik, P., & Ricchi, M. (2017). A Basic Guide to Real Time PCR in Microbial Diagnostics: Definitions, Parameters, and Everything. Frontiers in Microbiology, 8. https://doi.org/10.3389/fmicb.2017.00108

Lange, C. R. (Ed.). (2020). Effects of Free and Complexed Quaternary Ammonium Surfactants on Aerobic Wastewater Treatment Processes Treating Poultry Processing Wastewater. https://doi.org/10.2175/193864718825157374

Leighton, M. (n.d.). Should You Have Bristle Worms in Your Aquarium? A Complete Fact Sheet, Breeding, Behavior, and Care Guide. Vivofish. Retrieved January 5, 2022, from https://www.vivofish.com/bristle-worms/

Lumen. (n.d.). Temperature and Microbial Growth | Microbiology. Lumen Learning. Retrieved January 4, 2022, from https://courses.lumenlearning.com/microbiology/chapter/temperature-and-microbial-growth/

Mehrani, M. J., Sobotka, D., Kowal, P., Ciesielski, S., & Makinia, J. (2020). The occurrence and role of Nitrospira in nitrogen removal systems. Bioresource Technology, 303, 122936. https://doi.org/10.1016/j.biortech.2020.122936

Microscope Cameras & Mega Pixels - Does It Matter? (n.d.). Microscope Central. https://microscopecentral.com/pages/microscope-cameras-mega-pixels-does-it-matter

Mountain Empire Community College. (n.d.-a). Lesson 6: Protozoa. ENV 295: Microbiology of Well and Spring Water II. Retrieved December 16, 2021, from https://water.mecc.edu/courses/ENV295Micro/lesson6_5.htm

Mountain Empire Community College. (n.d.-b). Lesson 7: Metazoa. ENV 295. Retrieved December 16, 2021, from https://water.mecc.edu/courses/ENV295Micro/Lesson7_print.htm

Muirhead, W. M., & Appleton, R. (2007). Operational Keys to Nitrite Lock. Brown and Caldwell. https://brownandcaldwell.com/papers-and-reports/operational-keys-to-nitrite-lock/

Myszograj, S., Stadnik, A., & Płuciennik-Koropczuk, E. (2018). The Influence of Trace Elements on Anaerobic Digestion Process. Civil and Environmental Engineering Reports, 28(4), 105–115. https://doi.org/10.2478/ceer-2018-0054

Nielsen, J. L., Thomsen, T. R., and Nielsen, P. H. (2003.) Bacterial composition of activated sludge: Importance for floc and sludge properties. Conference paper. Retrieved November 20, 2021, from https://www.osti.gov/etdeweb/servlets/purl/20407952.

Nielsen, P. H., Daims, H., Lemmer, H., Arslan-Alaton, I., & Olmez-Hanci, T. (2009a). FISH Handbook for Biological Wastewater Treatment. Van Haren Publishing.

Nielsen, P. H., Kragelund, C., Seviour, R. J., & Nielsen, J. L. (2009b). Identity and ecophysiology of filamentous bacteria in activated sludge. FEMS Microbiology Reviews, 33(6), 969–998. https://doi.org/10.1111/j.1574-6976.2009.00186.x

Nkwonta, O., & Ochieng, G. (2009). Roughing filter for water pre-treatment technology in developing countries: A review. International Journal of Physical Sciences, 4(9). https://www.researchgate.net/publication/237827490_Roughing_filter_for_water_pre-treatment_technology_in_developing_countries_A_review

O&M News. (2003). Using state point analysis to maximize secondary clarifier performance. Retrieved November 24, 2021, from https://www.maine.gov/dep/water/wwtreatment/state_point_article.pdf.

Pedersen, L. F., Pedersen, P. B., Nielsen, J. L., & Nielsen, P. H. (2009). Peracetic acid degradation and effects on nitrification in recirculating aquaculture systems. Aquaculture, 296(3–4), 246–254. https://doi.org/10.1016/j.aquaculture.2009.08.021

Pennsylvania Department of Environmental Protection. (2014a.) Module 16: The activated sludge process part II. Training Module. Retrieved November 21, 2021, from https://files.dep.state.pa.us/water/bsdw/OperatorCertification/TrainingModules/ww16_sludge_2_wb.pdf.

Pennsylvania Department of Environmental Protection. (2014b.) Module 18: The activated sludge process part IV. Training Module. Retrieved November 22, 2021, from https://files.dep.state.pa.us/water/bsdw/operatorcertification/TrainingModules/ww18_sludge_4_wb.pdf.

Protozoa: The Naked Amoeba. (n.d.). Micrographia. Retrieved December 16, 2021, from https://www.micrographia.com/specbiol/protis/homamoeb/amoe0100.html

Quail, M., Smith, M. E., Coupland, P., Otto, T. D., Harris, S. R., Connor, T. R., Bertoni, A., Swerdlow, H. P., & Gu, Y. (2012). A tale of three next generation sequencing platforms: comparison of Ion torrent, pacific biosciences and illumina MiSeq sequencers. BMC Genomics, 13(1), 341. https://doi.org/10.1186/1471-2164-13-341

Respiration in bacteria: Microbiology. Biology Discussion. (2016, November 28). Retrieved November 20, 2021, from https://www.biologydiscussion.com/bacteria/respiration-in-bacteria-microbiology/63883.

Rich, L. G. (2003). NITRITES AND THEIR IMPACT ON EFFLUENT CHLORINATION. Lagoon Systems in Maine. Retrieved December 27, 2021, from http://www.lagoonsonline.com/technote4.htm#:%7E:text=Thu%2C%20a%20nitrite%20concentration%20of,of%20about%2050%20mg%2FL.&text=This%20suggests%20that%2C%20if%20insufficient,well%2Dmixed%20chlorine%20contact%20basin.

Richard, M. (1993). Practical Control Methods for Activated Sludge Bulking and Foaming - NYS Dept. of Environmental Conservation. New York State Department of Environmental Conservation. https://www.dec.ny.gov/chemical/34373.html

Richard, M. (2003, June 8). ACTIVATED SLUDGE MICROBIOLOGY PROBLEMS AND THEIR CONTROL [Paper Presentation]. 20th Annual USEPA National Operator Trainers Conference, Buffalo, NY. https://www.dec.ny.gov/docs/water_pdf/drrichard1.pdf

Richard, M. (2003). MICROBIOLOGICAL AND CHEMICAL TESTING FOR TROUBLESHOOTING LAGOONS. Lagoon Systems in Maine. http://www.lagoonsonline.com/trouble-shooting-wastewater-lagoons.html

Ripple, W. (2003). Pushing the Limits of Cold Temperature Nitrification. Lagoon Systems in Maine. Retrieved December 21, 2021, from http://www.lagoonsonline.com/ripple3.htm#:~:text=Cold%20Temperature%20Nitrification&text=Concerns%20about%20cold%20temperature%20nitrification,ammonia%20tend%20to%20go%20drmant.

Rizal, N. S. M., Neoh, H. M., Ramli, R., A. L. K Periyasamy, P. R., Hanafiah, A., Samat, M. N. A., Tan, T. L., Wong, K. K., Nathan, S., Chieng, S., Saw, S. H., & Khor, B. Y. (2020). Advantages and Limitations of 16S rRNA Next-Generation Sequencing for Pathogen Identification in the Diagnostic Microbiology Laboratory: Perspectives from a Middle-Income Country. Diagnostics, 10(10), 816. https://doi.org/10.3390/diagnostics10100816

Rossetti, S., Tomei, M. C., Nielsen, P. H., & Tandoi, V. (2005). "Microthrix parvicella", a filamentous bacterium causing bulking and foaming in activated sludge systems: a review of current knowledge. FEMS Microbiology Reviews, 29(1), 49–64. https://doi.org/10.1016/j.femsre.2004.09.005

Rumbaugh, E. (2018, April 12). Multicellular indicator organisms - rotifers, nematodes, tardigrades - Are they a good or bad in wastewater treatment systems? BIOLOGICAL WASTE TREATMENT EXPERT. Retrieved December 16, 2021, from https://www.biologicalwasteexpert.com/blog/multicellular-indicator-organisms-rotifers-nematodes-tardigrades-are-they-a-good-or-bad-in-wastewater-treatment-systems

Rumbaugh, E. (2014, July 2). Anaerobic Waste Treatment - Advantages/Disadvantages. BIOLOGICAL WASTE TREATMENT EXPERT. Retrieved December 23, 2021, from https://www.biologicalwasteexpert.com/blog/anaerobic-waste-treatment-advantagesdisadvantages

Science Direct. (n.d.-a). Krebs Cycle - an overview | ScienceDirect Topics. https://www.sciencedirect.com/topics/engineering/krebs-cycle

Science Direct. (n.d.). Membrane Fouling - an overview | ScienceDirect Topics. Retrieved December 23, 2021, from https://www.sciencedirect.com/topics/chemical-engineering/membrane-fouling

Seifi, M., & Fazaelipoor, M. H. (2012). Modeling simultaneous nitrification and denitrification (SND) in a fluidized bed biofilm reactor. Applied Mathematical Modelling, 36(11), 5603–5613. https://doi.org/10.1016/j.apm.2012.01.004

Sivasubramanian, R., Chen, G. H., & Mackey, H. R. (2021). The effectiveness of divalent cation addition for highly saline activated sludge cultures: Influence of monovalent/divalent ratio and specific cations. Chemosphere, 274, 129864. https://doi.org/10.1016/j.chemosphere.2021.129864

Smith, R. (2021, August). Implementation of Solids Retention Time Control in Wastewater Treatment. YSI. Retrieved December 21, 2021, from https://www.ysi.com/ysi-blog/water-blogged-blog/2018/10/implementation-of-solids-retention-time-control-in-wastewater-treatment

Speirs, L. B. M., Rice, D. T. F., Petrovski, S., & Seviour, R. J. (2019). The Phylogeny, Biodiversity, and Ecology of the Chloroflexi in Activated Sludge. Frontiers in Microbiology, 10. https://doi.org/10.3389/fmicb.2019.02015

Spuhler, D. (2020). Advanced Integrated Ponds. SSWM. https://sswm.info/water-nutrient-cycle/wastewater-treatment/hardwares/semi-centralised-wastewater-treatments/advanced-integrated-ponds

Sutton, S. (2006, February). Gram Staining. The Microbiology Network Inc. http://microbiologynetwork.com/the-gram-stain.asp

Táncsics, A., Farkas, M., Horváth, B., Maróti, G., Bradford, L. M., Lueders, T., & Kriszt, B. (2019). Genome analysis provides insights into microaerobic toluene-degradation pathway of Zoogloea oleivorans BucT. Archives of Microbiology, 202(2), 421–426. https://doi.org/10.1007/s00203-019-01743-8

Tarayre, C., Nguyen, H. T., Brognaux, A., Delepierre, A., de Clercq, L., Charlier, R., Michels, E., Meers, E., & Delvigne, F. (2016). Characterisation of Phosphate Accumulating Organisms and Techniques for Polyphosphate Detection: A Review. Sensors, 16(6), 797. https://doi.org/10.3390/s16060797

The Engineering Toolbox. (2018). Nitrogen - Density and Specific Weight vs. Temperature and Pressure. Retrieved January 4, 2022, from https://www.engineeringtoolbox.com/nitrogen-N2-density-specific-weight-temperature-pressure-d_2039.html

The Environmental Protection Agency. (2014, December). Priority Pollutant List. https://www.epa.gov/sites/default/files/2015-09/documents/priority-pollutant-list-epa.pdf

The International Water Association. (n.d.). Sequencing Batch Reactor. IWA Publications. Retrieved December 23, 2021, from https://www.iwapublishing.com/news/sequencing-batch-reactor

The Smithsonian. (2021, May 21). Water Bears Can Survive Impact Speeds of 1,845 Miles Per Hour. Smithsonian Magazine. https://www.smithsonianmag.com/smart-news/scientists-fired-water-bears-gun-test-their-survivability-upon-impact-180977784/

Thermo Fisher Scientific. (n.d.). Cell Viability Assays. Retrieved December 17, 2021, from https://www.thermofisher.com/nl/en/home/life-science/cell-analysis/cell-viability-and-regulation/cell-viability.html

Trygar, R. Understanding alkalinity. (2014, May). Treatment Plant Operator. Retrieved November 22, 2021, from https://www.tpomag.com/editorial/2014/05/understanding_alkalinity.

Trygar, R. MCRT, SRT, DSRT: What's it all about? (2014, June). Treatment Plant Operator. Retrieved November 23, 2021, from https://www.tpomag.com/editorial/2014/06/mcrt_srt_dsrt_whats_it_all_about.

Trygar, R. What the heck is SVI? (2010, March). Treatment Plant Operator magazine. Retrieved November 24, 2021, from https://www.tpomag.com/editorial/2010/03/what-the-heck-is-svi.

Tryger, R. (2011, October). It's Not Black Magic. Treatment Plant Operator. https://www.tpomag.com/editorial/2011/10/its_not_black_magic

United States Environmental Protection Agency. (1999). Wastewater Technology Fact Sheet: Sequencing Batch Reactors (EPA 932-F-99-073). https://www3.epa.gov/npdes/pubs/sbr_new.pdf

United States Environmental Protection Agency. (2011, August). Principals of Design and Operations of Wastewater Treatment Pond Systems for Plant Operators, Engineers, and Managers (EPA/600/R-11/088). https://www.epa.gov/sites/default/files/2014-09/documents/lagoon-pond-treatment-2011.pdf

United States Environmental Protection Agency. (2015, October). Anaerobic Digestion and its Applications (EPA/600/R-15/304). https://www.epa.gov/sites/default/files/2016-07/documents/ad_and_applications-final_0.pdf

University of Toronto. (n.d.). Cell Viability – Temerty Faculty of Medicine Flow Cytometry Facility. Temerty Faculty of Medicine Flow Cytometry Facility. https://flowcytometry.utoronto.ca/applications/cell-viability/

USP Technologies. (2021, March 2). Calcium Nitrate: Nitrate Applications for Hydrogen Sulfide Control. https://www.usptechnologies.com/calcium-nitrate/?gclid=CjwKCAjwoP6LBhBlEiwAvCcthOVomm3ozNPLBGCJNMBbGjmFAy5PPTOZmNP2ywMweykxzyWppZ9cxoC5XlQAvD_BwE

Utah State University Extension. Alkalinity and hardness: What is alkalinity? Water Quality Discussion. (n.d.). Retrieved November 21, 2021, from https://extension.usu.edu/waterquality/learnaboutsurfacewater/propertiesofwater/alkalinity.

Veolia. (n.d.). Activated sludge treatment with pure oxygen (UNOX® System). Veolia in Japan. Retrieved January 4, 2022, from https://www.veolia.jp/en/shiyeneirong/chanyexiangke/epc/activated-sludge-treatment-pure-oxygen-unox-system

Wang, L., Fan, D., Chen, W., & Terentjev, E. M. (2015). Bacterial growth, detachment and cell size control on polyethylene terephthalate surfaces. Scientific Reports, 5(15159). https://doi.org/10.1038/srep15159

Wastewater Blog. State point analysis. (2017, Mar.) Blog post. Retrieved November 23, 2021, from https://www.thewastewaterblog.com/single-post/2016/09/28/state-point-analysis.

Wikipedia contributors. (2021a, October 7). Flagellate. Wikipedia. https://en.wikipedia.org/wiki/Flagellate

Wikipedia contributors. (2021b, November 8). Rotifer. Wikipedia. https://en.wikipedia.org/wiki/Rotifer

Wikipedia contributors. (2021c, November 27). Ciliate. Wikipedia. https://en.wikipedia.org/wiki/Ciliate

Wikipedia contributors. (2021d, November 28). Nematode. Wikipedia. https://en.wikipedia.org/wiki/Nematode

Wikipedia contributors. (2021e, November 29). Polychaete. Wikipedia. https://en.wikipedia.org/wiki/Polychaete

Wikipedia contributors. (2021f, December 8). Tardigrade. Wikipedia. https://en.wikipedia.org/wiki/Tardigrade

Wisconsin Department of Natural Resources Bureau of Science Services. (1992a.) Advanced Anaerobic Digestion Study Guide. Training Module. Retrieved November 22, 2021, from https://dnr.wi.gov/regulations/opcert/documents/wwsganaerobdigadv.pdf.

Wisconsin Department of Natural Resources Bureau of Science Services. (1992b.) Introduction to Anaerobic Digestion Study Guide. Training Module. Retrieved November 22, 2021, from https://dnr.wi.gov/regulations/opcert/documents/wwsganaerobdigintro.pdf.

Wisconsin Department of Natural Resources Bureau of Science Services. (2010.) Advanced Activated Sludge Study Guide. Training Module. Retrieved November 23, 2021, from https://dnr.wi.gov/regulations/opcert/documents/wwsgactsludgeadv.pdf.

Wisconsin Department of Natural Resources. (2016a, February). Advanced Wastewater Study Guide. Retrieved December 21, 2021, from https://dnr.wi.gov/regulations/opcert/documents/StudyGuideAdvancedWastewater.pdf

Wisconsin Department of Natural Resources. (2016b, May 25). Nutrient Removal: Total Phosphorus subclass P. Wisconsin Department of Natural Resources Wastewater Operator Certification. https://dnr.wi.gov/regulations/opcert/documents/StudyGuidePhosphorus.pdf

Wisconsin Department of Natural Resources. (2018, October). Nutrient Removal - Total Nitrogen Study Guide. https://dnr.wi.gov/topic/opcert/documents/StudyGuideNutrientRemovalTotalNitrogen.pdf

Wisconsin Department of Natural Resources. (2016, February). Biological Treatment - Attached-Growth Processes Study Guide Subclass A2. https://dnr.wi.gov/topic/opcert/documents/StudyGuideAttachedGrowth.pdf

Wisconsin Department of Natural Resources. (2018, October). Anaerobic Treatment of Liquid Waste (No. A5). https://dnr.wi.gov/topic/opcer/documents /StudyGuideAnaerobicTreatmentofLiquidWaste.pdf

World Water Works. (n.d.). inDENSE - Selective Sludge Wasting - Technologies - World Water Works. Retrieved January 6, 2022, from https://www.worldwaterworks.com/technologies/indense

YSI. (n.d.). YSI Parameter Series: Dissolved Oxygen. YSI.Com. https://www.ysi.com/parameters/dissolved-oxygen

Zhang, J., Ding, X., Guan, R., Zhu, C., Xu, C., Zhu, B., Zhang, H., Xiong, Z., Xue, Y., Tu, J., & Lu, Z. (2018). Evaluation of different 16S rRNA gene V regions for exploring bacterial diversity in a eutrophic freshwater lake. Science of The Total Environment, 618, 1254–1267. https://doi.org/10.101/j.scitotenv.2017.09.228

Printed in the USA
CPSIA information can be obtained
at www.ICGtesting.com
LVHW062025100124
768663LV00002B/33